PRAISE FOR DARA KURTZ

**Author of *Crush Cancer* and
Creator of Crazy Perfect Life**

"Dara is an amazing human being who has found a way to help others through the experience of her own adversities." – Steven Aitchison, personal development guru and creator of Your Digital Formula

"I love the way Dara is positive and inspiring. She shows each of us how we can find meaning in everyday life and shares the insights she learned when going through a challenging time in her life." – Karen Salmansohn, author of *Think Happy*

"Dara can take the profound and make it accessible and can take the simple and make it significant. Her writing and her way of approaching life's everyday experiences as well as its big challenges and questions always give me food for thought." – Keith Wells, writer and creator of Great Lives Are Made

"Dara provides the daily reminder to all of us to live an inspired life. Her wit, empathy and realness shine through every page. She can find meaning in carpool. That's some amazing feat! We could all use a little Crazy Perfect Life in our lives." – Dr. Catherine Perlman, founder of The Family Coach and author of *Ignore It!*

"Dara is a perfect and shining example of how you can't let an illness get you down or stop you. She is an inspiration to all of us." – Iva Ursano, founder of the Amazing Me Movement

"Dara's personal story is both inspirational and life-transforming for anyone committed to living life to the fullest." – Zane Baker, CEO and co-founder of Valhalla Mind

"As a stage 4 cancer survivor, I can only recommend the beautiful and encouraging words from Dara." – Barbara Vercruysse, life and business coach and creator of Start the Life of Your Dreams

"Dara is one of those incredible characters who never fails to inspire those who cross her path in life." – Steve Waller, founder of A Conscious Rethink

"Dara's Crazy Perfect Life is the essence of what life is all about, and Dara infuses love and celebration and inspiration through her words of wisdom making the absolute most of every day, every MINUTE!" – Maria Flynn, creator of One Wise Life

"Dara's style of writing connects with what the average person is going through, but she takes it to a level that leaves the reader feeling a sense of hope that we really are in this together." – Aimee Halpin, author of *The Burned Hand*

"Want to be uplifted and learn how to focus on what's really important in life? Dara's thought-provoking stories and entertaining writing is a refreshing reminder of how to find meaning in each day." – Scott Colby, founder of Say It With Gratitude.

CRUSH CANCER

PERSONAL ENLIGHTENMENT FROM A CANCER SURVIVOR

DARA KURTZ

FOREWORD BY GARTH CALLAGHAN
AUTHOR OF *NAPKIN NOTES*

Published by Publish Pros
www.publishpros.com

This book is dedicated to my two daughters, Zoe and Avi. I hope your lives are filled with love, joy, peace and laughter. May you always have the ability to notice all the blessings in your life. Remember, even when life gets hard, it's always worth fighting for. And, to my husband, Jon, for sharing your life with me, for loving me unconditionally, flaws and all, and for helping me be the best version of myself. I love you with all my heart.

GET THE COMPANION WORKBOOK!

WWW.CRAZYPERFECTLIFE.COM/WORKBOOK

Whether you are currently dealing with a diagnosis and treatment or have been a survivor for years, you likely have some unresolved issues regarding this unwelcome chapter in your life.

The 100 journal exercises included in this companion workbook were devised to help you face your fears, manage your anxiety, guilt and anger, and, ultimately, appreciate the lessons this difficult experience can teach you.

Are you ready to crush cancer? Let's get started!

TABLE OF CONTENTS

SECTION 1

SECTION 2

FOREWORD

author of *Napkin Notes*

"I'm sorry. You have a tumor on your left kidney. It is most likely cancer, and it looks like it has spread. If it has spread, the mortality rate is very high."

My body shut down as the doctor started his sentence. My eyes lost focus and there was a loud din in my ears. I don't think I was fully conscious for the next 45 minutes. I could only think about death.

How do you bounce back from this conversation?

You don't, at least not right away. You can hope to be able to bounce sideways, or rebound a little, but bouncing back? That takes some time.

I have been writing notes to my daughter, Emma, for years. It started in kindergarten. I wanted to make her lunch a little special. I'd look for things to put in it that would let Emma know I was paying attention to her.

And, if I were totally honest, I was jealous. I worked and didn't spend nearly as much time with her as my wife, Lissa, could. I missed out on a lot of time with Em. If I could get her to think about me, about our father-daughter relationship, for even just a few more seconds each day, it was worth it. If she learned to love the notes, maybe she could understand the depth of my love for her.

I didn't know she cared about the notes until Emma was in second grade. One morning, I had finished making her lunch but hadn't yet written a note. Emma grabbed her lunch bag, noticed the absence of a note, marched over to me as she held up the open bag and stated two simple words, "Napkin note." I was blown away. Not only was she paying attention to the notes, she wanted more! Although I didn't need encouragement, I vowed to make this a regular practice. I learned as Emma and her friends moved up through school, some of her friends would sneak a peek into her lunch bag to read the note before lunchtime.

On the morning of her first day of school in eighth grade, I hesitated. Emma, was, after all, growing up. Would she still want a note at this point? I had a few moments of doubt. I decided to go ahead and write the note anyway. I am a note writer. I was consistent and if anything, writing a note even when Emma might not want one would show her my consistency and presence. I would always be there for her. Later that evening, Emma shared with me her lunch conversation with a friend. Emma had pulled out her lunch items one by one, including her napkin. Her friend saw the note and asked about it. Emma replied simply, "Oh, my dad makes my lunch every day and he writes me a note."

Her friend turned to her and said, "I am so jealous."

Why do we crave these tangible pieces of communication? It's simple, really. They are a reminder that we matter.

Don't wait to tell the people in your life that they matter. You have been given the gift of time, starting right now.

What do you do with that time? How do you use it? You do what you should have been doing all along.

Take each day as a gift.

Build relationships.

Make that phone call.

Write that note.

Remember that people matter. Actually, people and relationships are all that matter.

It turns out not only did I have cancer, but I would be diagnosed with cancer four times over the course of a few years. Each new diagnosis was a new struggle to face, and a new opportunity for me to build relationships. I share my story because I know how important it is to take the time to connect with those we love while we're still here.

Like Dara, I hope my story inspires and motivates people to make the most of each day of their lives. It truly is the connections we have with people that make our lives meaningful.

In his best-selling book, *Napkin Notes*, Garth Callaghan inspires and motivates people to connect daily with the ones they love. Visit Garth online at www.NapkinNotesDad.com.

PREFACE

I'll never forget the day I found out I had cancer, and to be honest, I don't want to. I also don't want to forget what I learned, what I went through and what I saw on my journey. You see, some lessons are too valuable to ever forget and I never want to live one single day without the appreciation and gratitude my cancer diagnosis taught me.

Whatever you're facing, I'm glad you're here. I'm honored to share my experience with you and hopefully help you on your own journey. You might be someone who has just been diagnosed with cancer and you're dealing with the initial shock and disbelief. Maybe you're someone who has been fighting cancer for many years. You may not have been diagnosed at all, but are dealing with the diagnosis of a friend or family member. Perhaps you're scared or confused or don't know what to do. You may even be seriously pissed off. I get it. It can be incredibly hard to stay positive and count your blessings while dealing with this difficult situation, especially if you don't feel well and just getting through each day seems overwhelming.

Whether you're going through a personal health struggle or watching a family member cope, I hope this book will make things a little easier. I went through a lot, took it all in and learned some important lessons along the way, which I'm going to share with you. I've never been the kind of person who holds back, and I'm certainly not going to start now. In this book, you'll get the good, the bad and everything in between. It's all here for the taking.

Section 1 shares my journey through treatment and provides specific takeaways you can begin using immediately if you or someone you know is currently dealing with cancer. Section 2 is all about moving forward after treatment, a particularly challenging but often overlooked time in the cancer experience. This section will help anyone who wants to live life to the fullest and find meaning in everyday living. At the end of each chapter, advice is given both for patients and for friends and family members who are walking this journey with their loved ones (the patient's tribe). These tips are given to help you not only get through this difficult time, but also hopefully emerge on the other side stronger and wiser, equipped to handle whatever life tosses your way.

When you or someone you care about is facing cancer, everything gets turned upside down. You almost don't recognize yourself or your loved ones anymore. An illness can change your physical appearance—zapping your energy and depleting your resources—and it can rock your mental strength to the core. While life around you goes on normally for other people, nothing is normal when you or someone you love is the one with cancer. It can also be extremely difficult to go back to living your life once you finish going through active treatment. This is how I felt months after I finished my treatment plan for breast cancer. My body might have been deemed "treated," but mentally I still had a long journey ahead of me. I felt anxious and vulnerable and I didn't know what to do or where to turn. I was doing the best I could to go to counseling and work through the fear, but it was hard. Sadly, there was no quick fix, no pill I could take. I had to make peace with what had happened to me, no one could do it for me. I hope this book helps you find your peace.

Much love,

Dara

SECTION 1

HOW TO GET THROUGH A CANCER DIAGNOSIS

SECTION 1: INTRODUCTION

For a long time, I had a picture in my mind of how my life would go. I never considered there would be a deviation from this plan. I knew bad things happened to good people, but I never thought anything would happen to me, especially not while I was young. Looking back, I realize how conceited my attitude was. How presumptuous I was in my thinking. You see, cancer has a way of humbling everyone it touches. It can seep into your life when you least expect it, an unwelcome guest who takes over. It doesn't care who you are, what you have going on in your life or how busy you are. Before cancer, I moved through life at a fast pace, checking things off my to-do list and not taking the time to notice all the blessings around me.

It's easy to take what you have for granted and not see how fortunate you truly are, especially if you assume life will continue as it is. I was happy with the status quo of my life and thought it would last forever.

It took a cancer diagnosis to wake me up. It felt like someone had punched me in the stomach and I couldn't catch my breath. It was an unfamiliar, frightening, horrible feeling, one I wouldn't wish on anyone. If you have been diagnosed with cancer, you may be feeling this way too.

Remember, you aren't alone. I'm here to walk with you through your journey. You might not like everything about your current situation, but there are blessings in your life even now, and I'm going to help you see them. You deserve to make the most of your life, regardless of the challenges you find yourself facing.

Sometimes life can be hard.
Sometimes life can feel
overwhelming.
Don't give up.
It's in these moments, when
we're tested, that we find out
how strong we truly are.

CHAPTER 1

MY STORY

It happened to me.

I was ushered into a small room and told to wait on the couch for the doctor. She would be in shortly to go over the results of my ultrasound and mammogram. How nice, I thought, I won't have to spend the weekend worrying about anything.

Not that I was really worried. I had gone for my annual mammogram several months back and everything had been fine. In fact, I had planned to return to work after this follow-up appointment. I was busy and didn't really have time for this, but when the appointment was made, the doctor did sound like it was necessary. She was just being extra careful, and it was good to be careful.

I had gone to my doctor because I couldn't shake a cold and I never get sick. After the cough lingered for weeks, I finally caved in and begrudgingly went to the morning on-call clinic at the office for some medication. They say you shouldn't take antibiotics unless you really need them, but I really needed them this time. While there, I happened to mention a strange lump I had noticed a few months earlier. It had actually been there longer, but it had started to get a little bigger. When I showed it to the doctor writing my prescription, she seemed a little caught off-guard. I left the office not just with my antibiotics, but also a strong suggestion to either let them schedule an appointment for an ultrasound and mammogram or call my OB/GYN asap.

"I'll take care of it," I said, "You don't need to schedule it for me."

As I got into my car, something told me to listen to what this doctor had said. I hit the speed dial on my phone and got an appointment with my OB/GYN right away, which led to an immediate ultrasound and mammogram. It was good to be extra vigilant.

I've had several friends who have been through false alarms with breast cancer, and I couldn't imagine ever having cancer myself. I didn't even mention the appointment to my husband because it seemed pointless. I would regret this decision later.

After the tests, I found myself sitting on an ugly couch hearing a doctor use words like "mass," "very concerned," and "70% chance of being cancer."

"You think I have cancer?" I asked the doctor.

She looked at me and nodded her head. "We'll need to schedule a biopsy."

"A biopsy?"

As she explained the process I just sat there, trying to take in what she was saying but not really hearing the words.

"I have to do this as soon as possible," I said to the doctor. I was now openly crying and my hands were shaking.

I was in shock, and I was alone.

Things were happening that shouldn't be and I wasn't prepared to deal with them. What should have been a quick, "just being extra careful" appointment was turning into a nightmare.

I wanted to have the biopsy immediately but that wasn't possible. Apparently there were many women in my situation and I was lucky to even get an appointment the following week. I left the office in a daze. I didn't go back to work. Somehow, I drove myself home, got into bed, and called my husband and best friend. I sat under the covers and cried. It was a Friday afternoon, I was 42, and I had just been told I probably had cancer.

"Don't jump to conclusions," my husband said. "You don't know anything yet."

But I didn't have to wait for the biopsy results. I just knew I had cancer.

This is how it happens, I thought. One minute you're fine, rushing your kids to school, worrying about what color to paint the kitchen, then in the blink of an eye, you're sitting on an ugly couch being told you probably have cancer.

How could I have cancer?

I had always been very health-conscious and watched everything I put into my body. I actually counted the number of servings of fruits and vegetables I ate each day. Seriously. I took pride in usually exceeding the required number. I did P90X, exercised at least five times a week and never had a weight issue.

I spent the weekend crying behind closed doors. I told my kids my allergies were bothering me and, of course, they believed me. Why wouldn't they? The house was a wreck, I couldn't eat and I didn't really care if homework was being done. I googled everything I could think of. There are some pretty scary cancer stories online, and I stumbled across every one of them. I memorized statistics, stages and treatment plans. I read heartbreaking stories of moms who had fought breast cancer and lost. I hugged my children tighter, snuggled with my husband longer and cried. I didn't know what I had or how bad it would be. I just knew I had breast cancer.

The waiting was torture. How do you tell someone you think they have cancer and then tell them they have to wait to find out? I needed information and I didn't want to wait to get it. I tried everything I could to move the biopsy to an earlier appointment, but it wasn't possible. They were fully booked. Every appointment was taken. The not knowing was practically impossible to live with.

Not knowing what was really going on.

Not knowing what I had to deal with.

Not knowing what was happening inside my body.

"Why are you doing this to yourself?" my husband asked. "You don't know you have cancer. You might not. You're putting yourself through hell and you're probably fine."

"I can understand why you're saying that," I said, "But I really think I do, and I need to know what I have. What I'm dealing with. What could happen."

My husband was smart enough not to argue with me.

To say I was unhinged is an understatement. I told very few of my friends and family what I was going through because I didn't want to worry anyone until I had an official diagnosis. I would look at my daughters and think, "How is this happening to my family? What if they're forced to grow up without me?"

The day of the biopsy finally arrived and I was relieved to be moving forward. This time my husband went with me. I'd learned my lesson, I wasn't going there alone. We were ushered into the same room I was in about a week earlier and sat on the same couch. I was nervous, but glad to be this much closer to knowing for sure. The waiting had been excruciating. I couldn't keep reading cancer stories and memorizing statistics. It wasn't serving me well and I was close to the edge.

The doctor performing the biopsy came into the room to go over the paperwork and happened to have a kid in my oldest daughter's class at school. He explained the process, then a nurse took me to the room where the biopsy would be done. I sat on the table and cried. I cried because I was afraid of what they would tell me. I cried because I kept thinking of everything I had read. I cried because this was happening to me and my family. The doctor came in, and as he performed the procedure he told me I needed to prepare myself because it looked like cancer. While I wasn't surprised by this since I had originally had that sick feeling in my gut, hearing him say it was still upsetting. I didn't realize it, but I had been holding on to hope. I wanted to be wrong. I wanted Jon to tell me, "See, you worried yourself for nothing. You should have listened to me."

But once a doctor says you probably have cancer, it's hard to maintain any amount of hope. In that instant, my greatest fear was realized and I didn't know what to do or where to turn. I cried on the table while one of the kindest doctors I'll ever meet consoled me. Later that evening he called to confirm I had breast cancer. He didn't think it had spread, but I would need more tests to determine whether or not the cancer was in other parts of my body. Gulp.

I had cancer. I kept saying it over and over again in my mind. I walked through the rest of the evening in a daze, trying not to act strange around my kids. It was hard, but we didn't want to tell them yet. We needed more facts and time to digest the news ourselves. Truth be told, I was in uncharted territory and my coping skills weren't as great as I would have liked. A doctor called in a prescription for Xanax for me, something I had never taken before. I needed something to take the edge off while I got used to the initial shock of having cancer.

I remember going to pick up the prescription and the pharmacist telling me, "You don't want to take this for very long because you might become addicted."

I think 30 pills were less than $3.00.

"Thanks for the advice," I said, "but I just got diagnosed with cancer and I need this right now."

How could I be strong for my kids when I was barely holding it together myself? We didn't want to tell them the "Big C" had entered their world. Not yet. Fortunately, the doctor who performed my biopsy, otherwise known as my angel, sped things up a bit and helped me get my other tests immediately. I think he understood what a mess I was. How there's only so much a girl can handle and I was at the end of my rope. There are people who enter your life at random times and who are there for you when you need them. Strangers who become part of your story because of what you go through with them. For me, the doctor who happened to be there that morning is someone I will always be grateful for.

Getting a cancer diagnosis is just the first step in a long, hard process of getting all the facts. Once we knew I had breast cancer, we had to wait for the pathology report to learn the specifics. Before I was diagnosed I didn't realize how many different types of one particular disease a person could have. For example, there are many different kinds of breast cancer. What type you have is very important and will directly impact your treatment plan. I went through a lot of tests and diagnostic exams and met with a slew of doctors to determine my exact situation and treatment plan. There's also a lot of waiting when you're collecting this information and the waiting is hard. It sucks, actually. I still hadn't told my kids or family and it was challenging to act normal around them while keeping my secret. A secret I didn't want to have.

I also learned there is some luck in cancer: in catching it early, in the type of cancer it is and in the amount of research that's been done. I was fortunate to have found my breast cancer relatively early, and it was the kind that offered me many treatment options and targeted therapies. But it was hard to feel lucky. From where I sat, I had become the mom everyone would feel sorry for, the mom in the carpool lane with cancer.

Once we had all the facts, it was time to share the news with our friends and family, and of course, our daughters. I sent a text message to my closest friends, telling them what I had and what my treatment plan was. I didn't want to talk to anyone, but a lot of people needed to know. My husband later sent out an email. We waited until my daughters—who were in fifth and eighth grade—came home from school to tell them. That was one of the worst days of my life.

"What's going on?" my oldest daughter, Zoe, asked. "You're acting really strange."

It was 3:30 p.m. on Friday, and Jon and I were home. Back then, we weren't both usually home that early.

"Let's go into the den," I gently said to them after they had eaten a snack.

"Ok," Zoe said. "But you're being weird. Does someone have cancer?"

She seriously asked us this question, and, before I could think about what to say, I burst into tears.

"What?" they both asked. "You have cancer?"

This is not the way I had anticipated the conversation going. I had imagined us sitting down and in a calm manner, telling them I had breast cancer but would be OK. Instead, I was a mess, which certainly wasn't making it any easier for them. In less than two minutes my daughters were forced to experience first-hand the uncertainty of life. Seeing the pain and fear in their eyes was heartbreaking. There's never a good time to get cancer, but getting it when you have young children is incredibly difficult. You want to keep your kids safe and out of harm's way. You want them to feel secure, especially in their home and with their family. I'll never forget the sound of my youngest daughter hyperventilating as she tried to process this world-crashing-down-on-her news. My kids had never gone through a personal crisis before, and it was hard for them to handle. They struggled to make sense of how I could be fine one day and have cancer the next. Truth be told, I was struggling as well. It didn't make sense.

For a long time, I worried about what my diagnosis would do to my children. I carried this guilt on my shoulders, feeling like it was my fault they were forced to see this unpleasant side of life. I finally realized I can't protect them from bad things happening. What I can do is show them when life presents challenges, as it always will, it's how a person deals with these challenges that really matters. Showing my kids that facing hard times head on, with a positive attitude and the will to fight, will serve them better than trying to protect and shelter them. Armed with these necessary tools, they'll have a much better chance of overcoming whatever life tosses their way. While I would never have wanted them to have to learn this lesson at such young ages, I had to accept I couldn't do anything about it. I didn't figure this out until much later though. I had to learn to cope with my diagnosis before I could help my children.

The reality is, shit happens.

It had happened to my family.

And, maybe your family too.

While cancer has become a household word, pay attention to the experience your kids, family members and friends have had with it. Know where they're coming from. Your children might know someone who has passed away from cancer. My kids had two friends whose fathers had recently passed away from cancer. This was their experience with the "Big C." This meant they didn't trust I would be OK. Try to find people who have been through what you're facing and who have had positive outcomes. This will not only help your kids, it will also help you.

I was shocked at the number of people who contacted me, people who had been through cancer and survived and who reached out to me to offer help and support. I didn't realize how much I needed this. Hearing positive stories of people who had walked in my shoes and come out OK was exactly what I needed to hear. I was anxious and scared. I needed to talk with people who had survived. They gave me strength and made me feel like I might be able to get through this. I knew there were negative stories as well, but fortunately people were smart enough to keep these to themselves, at least in the beginning. There's a certain camaraderie between people who have gone through a cancer diagnosis. It's almost like a club (a club you don't want to join, but one you find yourself forced into), and the inspiration you will get from talking to people who have been down this path is incredibly helpful. Surround yourself with positive and uplifting scenarios that remind you other people have been through what you're facing and have won. Lots of people. According to the National Cancer Institute, by the year 2026, the projected number of cancer survivors will be over 20.3 million people. That's a lot of people.

You need to believe you can beat whatever it is you're facing, and positive reinforcement will definitely help. You must play to win and expect good things to happen. No one wants to hear the words, "You have cancer," and no one wants to watch someone they care about go through treatment for cancer. It will take a little time for the shock of the diagnosis to sink in. Try to take one day at a time and be patient with yourself. I'm sorry you have to deal with this. I wish I could wave a magic wand over your head or sprinkle pixie dust on you and make it go away, but I can't. What I can do, and what I will do, is tell you everything you need to know to help make your journey a little easier. Whatever happens, it's going to be OK. You can handle it. I know you don't want to, but you don't have a choice. Dammit.

TIP 1: GET THE FACTS

The hardest part is not knowing what you're dealing with. My mind came up with some pretty scary scenarios and I'm guessing your mind might be doing the same thing. Try hard not to jump to conclusions until you have a complete diagnosis. Believe me, I know this is much easier said than done. Try to do the opposite of what I did. I fell apart, was an absolute train wreck and could barely function. This was not helpful. In fact, it made things much harder. Stick with your normal routine while you're waiting for information and test results. Exercise, go to a movie, do whatever you need to do to distract yourself. There's really no use in jumping to conclusions until you have all the facts. But if you want to cry, do it. I made my life unnecessarily hard that long weekend when I could have enjoyed it with my family. Time is our most precious commodity. Don't waste your time with "what if" thoughts. Save it until you meet with the people in the white coats.

TIP 2: STOP GOOGLING UNTIL YOU HAVE AN EXACT DIAGNOSIS

I absolutely understand the desire to seek out information. Especially in the beginning when you're waiting for test results and don't know a lot about your situation. We're used to googling whatever it is we want to know, and if you're like me, you might be a little impatient. You want to try to diagnose yourself. You want to know what you have, what might happen to you and what the statistics are.

Stay off your computer. Seriously. Resist the urge. Don't read anything having to do with symptoms, stages or life expectancy. Everyone is different and only your doctors can tell you the specifics of your situation after they run a bunch of tests and get all the results back. I lost many nights of sleep reading depressing stories that didn't have anything to do with me.

Pinky swear you won't do this.

It's for your own good.

You'll thank me later.

If you absolutely can't stop the urge to google information and diagnose yourself, don't do it at night while you're in bed. The best way to ruin a good night's sleep is to look up anything having to do with cancer.

Once you get a specific diagnosis, you will want to do your research to figure out what your treatment options are, where you want to be treated, the doctors you will use and if you want to get a second or third opinion. Many hospitals have a cancer services department and nurse navigators who will be able to provide you with a wealth of information and give you suggestions. There are also many helpful online resources. It's perfectly fine to google away once the people in white coats diagnose you, just try to wait until they have all the facts and have shared them with you.

TIP 3: IT'S OK TO BE SERIOUSLY ANGRY. OR SAD. OR SCARED

Every cancer diagnosis is different, as is each person's experience. However, feelings of uncertainty, apprehension, fear and worry occur in the majority of people who are faced with one. Getting cancer sucks. You didn't ask for it and you certainly don't want it. But since you have it, you've got to deal with it. Pretending the "Big C" didn't happen to you or someone you love won't help. Instead, you have to face it head on. Channel your energy into coming up with a treatment plan you feel good about.

Let yourself cry. Scream. Yell. Do whatever you need to do to get your feelings out. It's OK to feel sorry for yourself or to be seriously pissed off. If you are both, congratulations, you're normal. You're probably dealing with all sorts of emotions, and that's OK, but it's also time to fight. Hard. We're on the same team now and we're in this together.

TIP 4: TELLING YOUR KIDS YOU HAVE CANCER

Wait until you have all the facts before you tell your kids about an illness you or someone they care about is facing. Fortunately, I had a very positive prognosis and was able to share this with my daughters. It was obviously easier to tell my kids I had cancer, and then in the next sentence, tell them I was expected to be OK. I've been asked many times how I would have handled the situation if my cancer had been advanced or my prognosis had been negative.

I imagine I would always present a hopeful scenario, because regardless of what someone is dealing with, there's always hope. Always. You don't go onto a battlefield expecting to surrender. You fight and you expect to win. However, the ages of your kids will impact your decision regarding how many details you share. Remember, kids are smart and they know how to use a computer. Maybe even better than you do. They can find the sad stories all over the internet just as easily as you can. We promised my daughters we would be honest with them and this seemed to help them manage their fear. I'm not going to lie to you, my diagnosis caused them a hell of a lot of anxiety.

We also asked one of my doctors to talk with our kids about my diagnosis and prognosis. Our kids were allowed to ask her anything they wanted to know and we would leave the room. It was an opportunity for them to get the answers to the questions they were afraid to ask me or my husband. Don't underestimate the power of hearing medical news from someone in a white coat. Ask your doctor to meet with your kids. The worst that can happen is they say no. My daughters found this incredibly helpful and reassuring.

Once the "Big C" enters your family's life, it causes fear and anxiety that will always be there, even after many years. I'm still amazed at how, several years later, something can happen that triggers a memory for one of my daughters and the feelings they experienced come flooding back. It is what it is.

TIP 5: GET IT OUT

You have to deal with your feelings, and the best way to do this is to force yourself to get them out. Keeping them all bottled up inside isn't going to help. In fact, it will probably make things much harder. For me, writing in a journal was a must, and something I recommend even if you aren't someone who tends to enjoy writing.

Get yourself a journal. Not next week, not a month from now. Today. It doesn't have to be fancy or expensive. Heck, just staple pieces of paper together and start writing. Consider this your new best friend. Start writing at the beginning of each day, before you even get dressed and move forward with your day. Grab a pen or pencil and just start writing. Write about how you feel. Write about your fears. Write about how pissed off you are because of what you're going through. Don't worry about what you're saying, how it looks or the spelling. No one is going to see it but you.

I started writing in my journal each morning and soon started turning to it again in the evening. It became a place to go when I didn't know where else to turn. It was helpful for me to write before I went to bed. I would get all of my scary thoughts out of my head, which would help me sleep a little better.

You might be surprised by how much you start writing once you get used to it. At first I didn't think I would have a lot to say and it felt awkward to write down my thoughts. But the more I did it, the more comfortable it became. It only took me a few weeks to realize I had pages and pages of thoughts inside me. In order for this to work, you must commit to it and practice it daily. Repetition is your friend here. You need a safe place where you can get out all of the anger, anxiety, fear and sadness inside of you. If you think you don't have any of these feelings and you don't need a journal, you're wrong. Do it. Today. If you have friends or family members going through cancer, go buy a journal for them. If you think I'm bossy, you aren't the first person to think that.

In all seriousness, only you know what will help you the most when you're going through a challenging experience. I recognize writing in a journal might not be your thing. I would definitely recommend you try it, but if it doesn't work, look for other ways to deal with your feelings. Maybe you would rather talk to your friends, spouse, nurse navigator or doctor. Perhaps playing sports would be the best way for you to deal with your emotions. Hit a punching bag, smack the hell out of a golf ball or tennis ball, or run your feelings out. Maybe painting or drawing is the way you express yourself. Here's the bottom line: You're facing a difficult challenge and you have to find a way to deal with your feelings. Ignoring them or pretending they don't exist isn't going to help.

What I liked about my journal is that I could write down things I might not be comfortable saying to another person. And when you're going through cancer, there will absolutely be times when you don't have the energy to exercise or play a sport. But you can take a journal with you anywhere, you can write in it even when you're tired and whatever you put in it is private.

TRIBE TIP

It's hard when someone you care about gets cancer. You might be trying to get used to the idea yourself and wanting to help them at the same time. As close as you are to your friend or family member, and as scared as you might be, you aren't the one going through it. It's not your diagnosis. While it might impact you significantly, try to focus on the needs of the person who received the diagnosis and take your cues from them. If they want to talk, be there to listen. If they want to have time alone, respect their need for privacy. If they want to have a pity party, be there with refreshments (I'm thinking wine or ice cream). This is particularly important in the beginning when the person is probably in shock and is trying to process everything that is happening.

Talk to your close friends and family about your personal feelings, but don't burden the person who was just diagnosed. Even though you don't mean to, telling them how scared or worried you are may make them feel guilty about what they are putting you through. The guilt will probably come anyway, so do everything you can not to add to it.

Don't be afraid to ask for help
when you need it.
Lean on other people.
We all have times in our lives
when the strength of other
people carries us forward.

CHAPTER 2

GET YOUR "A TEAM" TOGETHER

The best way for you to get through this difficult experience is to form a team of health care providers you have the utmost trust and faith in. This is your life and you need to have complete confidence in the people taking care of you. Don't just settle on a doctor, be willing to put a little time and effort into choosing who you want to work with. You will have some difficult decisions to make and you need to have doctors who are patient, kind and are willing to take the time to not only explain all of your options but also the research and statistics behind every option. It can be overwhelming, especially to someone who isn't used to medical terminology. Plus, it can be very stressful trying to adjust to the idea that you have cancer while feeling the pressure of deciding who you're going to work with and what treatment plan you want to follow.

When I originally found out I had cancer, my first thought was, "I want this out. Now. I don't want to wait." You might feel this way and want to just move forward without taking the time to research treatment options and doctors. In most cancer situations, it isn't necessary to immediately proceed with treatment, you'll have at least a small amount of time to carefully make decisions. Of course, you'll have to listen to the doctors regarding the urgency of your particular situation, but don't feel like you can't take a little time to digest the news and think things through.

How do you find the right doctors for you? You talk to other people who have conquered cancer. You get referrals from your primary doctor or other doctors you know or work with. You ask other people about the experiences they've had with the doctors they worked with. If the same name keeps coming up and you hear positive things from several people about the same person, this is a good sign. You can also go online and research the doctors in your area. Don't be afraid to meet with other doctors or get a second or third opinion. I didn't feel the need to get a second opinion. I felt very comfortable with my team of doctors and trusted them immediately.

But I'll never forget my doctor saying, "It's absolutely OK to get a second opinion. You won't hurt my feelings, I want you to be comfortable with your choice."

Her telling me this confirmed she was someone I could work with. The sign of a really good doctor is someone who doesn't mind if you get another opinion. Someone who doesn't feel challenged or threatened because you want to talk to someone else about your situation.

Make sure you have a doctor you can count on to be there when you need help. If you currently aren't comfortable picking up the phone and calling your doctor when something is bothering you or you're concerned about something, you need to chat with them about this. As I told my doctors, "You're my people and I'm trusting you with my life." If your doctor isn't receptive to your calls or concerns, you might want to consider finding another one. This is your health, your life, and you've got to have faith in who you're working with.

A lot of times there isn't an exact protocol to follow in terms of what your treatment plan should be. There might be different treatments available with varying risks, side effects and long-term benefits. Medicine isn't a black-and-white situation. There are a lot of varying factors to be considered to determine the best option for you. You never want to look back with any regrets, and sometimes you only have one shot to get it right. There will be lots of decisions to make, depending on what type of cancer you have and how advanced it is. You have to decide if you're going to have surgery and/or chemotherapy, which to do first, and if you're going to do radiation. There are even different kinds of chemo, and it can feel overwhelming. If you've picked doctors you really trust, let them make the call.

My attitude was, "I trust my doctors. They know I want to be as aggressive as possible. I'm not a doctor and I'm going to do what they say I need to do." I knew we were on the same page and they had my best interest at heart.

There are many cancer sites with research, statistics and information. These will also give you information on studies being conducted, and you can learn if you are a good candidate for certain protocols. The Mayo Clinic, MD Anderson Cancer Center, National Cancer Institute and American Cancer Society all have great websites, and there are many more. If the medical center where you're being treated tells you they can't help you or your cancer is too advanced and there's nothing left for you to do, the above websites can be particularly helpful in trying to find clinical research being conducted. Hopefully you've chosen a doctor who is up on all the latest research for the type of cancer you have. With the advancements in modern medicine, there are amazing discoveries being made all the time and new drugs being approved. There are also many websites dedicated to specific kinds of cancer. Again, it depends on what you're dealing with.

Whenever I met with a doctor and had to make a decision regarding my health, I always asked the following question, "If you were me and you were going through this, what would you do?" Several doctors told me they had never had a patient ask them that, which I found surprising. I told my doctors to think about themselves every time they made a decision for me. "Treat me like I'm you or your family member and always make decisions regarding my health based on what you would do for yourself or someone you loved." You deserve to have your doctor make conscientious decisions about your health, and this is a great way for them to approach it.

Don't be surprised if you need several doctors. I had a radiologist, surgeon, oncologist, plastic surgeon and radiation oncologist. Doesn't that seem crazy? Fortunately, I had a lot of friends in the medical community who were able to help me decide who I was going to work with. I never once questioned the care I received or the ability of any of my doctors. They saved my life and I will always be grateful for everything they did for me.

Once you commit to a plan, expect it to work. Whatever you're facing, regardless of the statistics, plan to be a success story. There are always success stories, so you might as well be one, right? Don't underestimate the power of having a good attitude and outlook. I know it's hard, but you must do everything you can to stay positive. We've already established that getting cancer sucks. Now, we just need to deal with it. One of the best ways you can take control is to get your team together and fight.

TIP 6: IT'S YOUR LIFE, YOU DO YOU

There will be people in your life who don't agree with the treatment you and your doctors decide on. Unfortunately, some of these people will probably voice their opinion to you and cause you to second-guess your decisions. You might even have close friends or family who don't agree with you. Some people will think you're being too aggressive, others will think you aren't doing enough. It doesn't matter. What matters is how you feel about your doctors and the plan they established for you.

You might hear comments such as, "My friend had that kind of cancer and she didn't have to do chemo, why do you?" or "You aren't having surgery? Why not?"

Again, as long as you're comfortable with what you're doing, it doesn't matter what other people think.

Here's what you need to remember: unless your friends and family have an MD at the end of their name and happen to specialize in oncology, their opinions don't really count. Seriously. Just thank them for their thoughts and truck on with whatever you and your doctors have decided. It's easy to get influenced by the people in your life who mean well, but you've got to resist and trust your medical team.

TRIBE TIP

My husband, Jon, who is an attorney, immediately got a yellow legal notepad and began writing down everything that was said each time we talked to a doctor. I wasn't in any condition to take notes, I was still just trying to process what was happening. This was extremely helpful because we could reference his notes later when we couldn't remember something that was said. If you can take your friend or family member to their doctor's appointments, at least in the beginning, it will be very helpful. Not only will you be able to provide support and encouragement, you will also be able to listen and know what's going on. It's nice to have a second set of ears listening to what's being said. The amount of information that's given, particularly when you're trying to get a handle on what you're dealing with, is significant. Jon even made a file for all of my test results and scans labeled "Dara's Cancer Diagnosis." Just what I wanted at age 42.

Give me the strength
to move forward
when I feel like
quitting and let me
remember to count
my blessings.
Even when I can't see them.

CHAPTER 3

WAS THIS REALLY HAPPENING?

When I was nine years old, my best friend's mom fought and lost her battle with breast cancer. I remember going to her house and seeing her mom as she was going through treatment. She struggled to get out of bed and spend time with us. I didn't really know what was going on, I just knew she was sick. That was over 30 years ago, when cancer wasn't a household name. Unfortunately, cancer has become part of our lives, and today it would be difficult to find someone who hasn't been touched by the disease. Almost everyone knows someone who has received a cancer diagnosis. We know people who have survived the disease and people who have, sadly, passed away.

My experience watching my friend's mom fight and lose her battle with cancer was still my reference point to breast cancer. When I first got diagnosed, I immediately recalled what I had seen and how it had ended. Only now I was an adult and was able to understand what she had faced and the despair and agony she must have felt. I couldn't believe I was now the mom with young kids facing the same disease my friend's mom had fought. The irony wasn't lost on me.

I still remember the day she passed away. We got a phone call early in the morning, and my mom called me into her bedroom. We sat on the bed and cried together as she told me the news. I was terrified the same thing would happen to her or my dad.

"Promise me you won't get cancer," I said to her as we held hands and cried. I couldn't understand why or how my friend's mom could get sick and die. I was scared and wanted to be told everything would be OK.

"I wish I could," my mom said to me, "But there aren't any guarantees for any of us. We have to make the most of the time we have together."

This wasn't the answer I had hoped to hear at the time, but looking back on it, I appreciate her honesty.

Fast-forward many years later. Cancer was in my life again, causing me fear and stealing my peace. I couldn't believe this was happening to me and my family. I kept asking myself what I had done wrong. I wondered if this was my fault. I needed someone to blame for my health crisis and I needed answers. Surely, there had to be a reason for this. A person doesn't go from being healthy to sick without a reason, right? Life had dealt me an unfair hand, as it had so many other people, and I wanted to make sense of it. Just as I had tried and failed to understand why my friend's mom had passed away at the young age of 39, I couldn't understand how I had been diagnosed with cancer.

I tried to process my diagnosis and get used to the idea. "I have cancer," I would say to myself.

Sometimes, in the early hours of the morning, I would wake up when everyone else in my family was sleeping. It was hard to ignore the little voice in my head when the house was quiet and I wasn't running from one doctor's appointment to the next. That's when the hard questions would come, the ones I tried to keep locked away. I didn't want to ask them because I wasn't ready to deal with the answers. During the day, I distracted myself and stayed busy. It was easier that way. I had people to talk me down off my ledge. But in the stillness of the night I couldn't keep the questions away. I heard them and they caused me a lot of anxiety.

"What if I die in surgery? What if my cancer comes back? What if my kids have to grow up without me?"

I was an emotional train wreck and would cry easily and openly. My world had been completely rocked and I didn't know how to find my way back. Everything I had thought about my life and all the plans I had for myself went out the window the moment I was diagnosed. I didn't know it then, but my life would forever be put into two categories: life before cancer (BC) and life after cancer (AC). What I now know is this: Once a person crosses from one category into the next, there's no going back. Ever. Thank you, cancer.

I always had a feeling I would get breast cancer. While I didn't think I would get it at age 42, I had already decided when cancer came knocking on my door I would be as aggressive as possible. I opted to have a double mastectomy with reconstruction and to have expanders put in at the same time. These would eventually be replaced with my new and improved boobs. I had always had a small chest and barely filled a size 32A bra. It seemed unfair that someone with such a small chest should even have to deal with breast cancer. I wanted my reconstruction to look natural and fit my body. Most importantly to me, I wanted to have the surgery as soon as possible because I found it unsettling to have cancer inside me. Overnight I went from a seemingly healthy person to someone with a team of doctors and the need for a living will.

I had projects I was working on at my office, but everything was put on hold. Work didn't seem very important anymore. I went from a busy person with a full life to a cancer patient focused on treatment plans, surgery, chemo and radiation. I had more doctor's appointments than I'd had in the rest of my life combined. It's amazing how quickly life can change. We know anything can happen to anyone at any time, but until it happens to you, you don't think about it. At least I didn't think about it. All of a sudden, just getting through the day took a lot of energy and effort.

The night before my surgery, my friends came over and took charge. They organized everything in my life and I happily let them take over. They set up schedules for meals and driving carpool and even organized people to come over and bring me lunch a few times each week. I thought this was a little excessive and I was embarrassed to be the person who needed this, but their love and support was a nice distraction. Each of my daughters gave me cards filled with the most beautiful words I've ever received. I still keep the cards in my nightstand and read them every once in a while. They're filled with heartfelt love from little girls who were terrified something would happen to their mom. I also wrote little notes to each of my daughters and to my husband, just in case I didn't survive the surgery. Maybe it was a little nutty, but it made me feel better. I couldn't control a lot of things, but I could take out a pen and a piece of paper and write something to the people

I loved. I still have the notes I wrote too, but I have never opened them. I'm counting on not needing them for a really long time.

On the day of the surgery, Jon and I still couldn't believe it was happening while the nurses tried to calm me and prepare me for surgery. For those of you who haven't had surgery, there's a stressful moment when you say goodbye to your loved ones and are wheeled into the operating room. Fortunately, they put you to sleep immediately, and the next thing you know you're being awakened by someone in the recovery room. I remember waking up to a nurse touching my head. He was stroking my hair and telling me I was going to be OK while I mumbled, "I'm going to throw up." I've had many surgeries since then and always ask for nausea medication to be put in my IV before they wake me up. I've never had a problem since. It's a good play, and one I recommend if you tend to get nauseous easily.

My surgery and recovery went well. I'm not going to say it was fun. I could think of a lot of other ways I would rather spend my time. Even cleaning toilets would have been better than having a double mastectomy with a side of reconstruction.

A few weeks later I was scheduled to start chemo. Before my treatments began, I had an appointment with the nurse to discuss the side effects of the different drugs they would be injecting into me. It felt like every time I asked a question I was told, "Everyone is different and we don't know how you'll react." This became my least favorite answer to any question. Although I know it was the truth, sometimes you don't want to hear the truth. Sometimes you just want your doctor to say, "Everything is going to be OK."

The potential side effects sounded horrible and I wondered why I was doing this to myself. I despise throwing up. I know it isn't something most people enjoy, but I have always had an abnormal aversion to vomiting. Having a fear of throwing up and being told you're about to be pumped full of drugs that cause nausea and vomiting isn't ideal. It's not like I didn't have enough things to worry about. Fortunately, there are incredible medications today, and I was given several prescriptions to help with nausea. I filled each and every one of those prescriptions and crossed my fingers one of them would work for me.

When I was told I would need chemo, one of the first questions I asked was if I would lose my hair. I admit, my hair was overly important to me. I spent a fortune getting it chemically straightened and the last thing I wanted was for it to fall out. I loved my hair and the thought of being bald made me sick. Hair is an especially important feature to many women. Research shows the way a teenage girl thinks about her hair directly impacts her self-esteem. Wanting my daughters to get used to me with short hair, I decided to cut it before it started to fall out. It was depressing, but there wasn't anything I could do about it. I reluctantly decided when I lost my hair I would wear a wig or baseball cap.

I didn't want to need a wig.

I didn't want to have to go through treatment.

I didn't want any of this.

On my first day of chemo, I remember looking around the waiting room and thinking to myself, "How did I get here?" But that's the thing, how did anyone else in the room get there? We were all different: various ages, races and stages of health. Cancer isn't picky. It will strike anyone.

The waiting room of the cancer center was eye-opening. I had never spent any time in a cancer center before my diagnosis and I wasn't used to seeing people who looked sick. I noticed some people struggling and figured they had been dealing with cancer and going through treatment for a long time. Other people were in wheelchairs or walked with a cane. Many people, like myself, looked healthy. Some people were crying, some were smiling, others were reading the Bible. A lot of patients had family members or friends with them. One person had an interpreter. People chatted and were friendly and everyone was on the same team. What I remember most about sitting in that room was the bravery I saw when I looked directly into the eyes of the patients. It takes courage to sit outside a chemo room and wait for your name to be called. I learned these people were soldiers on a battlefield about to go to war, and they were ready to fight. I didn't want to be one of these soldiers, but I didn't have a choice.

TIP 7: ACCEPT YOUR DIAGNOSIS

If you've just received a scary diagnosis and you're asking yourself why this happened to you, that's normal. You want answers. There's got to be a reason, right? Here's the thing, you will never understand why you were diagnosed with cancer. I thought about everything and anything I could come up with to help me figure out why this happened to me. I really wanted to blame something. To point my finger at someone. I never got very far. Life is random and sometimes shit happens. The sooner you can accept your current situation, the better. This doesn't mean you have to like it. I don't expect you to be happy about what you're facing. However,

I suggest you try very hard to accept whatever it is you're dealing with. Don't waste your energy trying to find someone to blame. Instead, spend your energy getting all the facts, taking care of yourself and getting better. Be productive and do things that help you feel good.

TIP 8: COUNT ON YOUR TRIBE

Let your friends help you. You can't do this alone. Accept that you need assistance and take people up on their offers to bring you dinner or help with housework, grocery shopping or carpool. Ditch your pride and just give in. If you don't have people you can count on, there are many nonprofit agencies who are happy to help. Most hospitals have a cancer services office that can also be a great place to seek assistance. This is the time to be good to yourself. You aren't weak because you need help from other people. Plus, if the situation were reversed and you knew someone was going through a difficult time, wouldn't you want to lend a helping hand? Of course you would. You have enough on your plate right now, and anything you do to make your life a little easier is a good thing. Save all the cards people send to you and read them when you're having a hard day. Keep a list of the nice things people do for you so you can eventually write thank you notes. I still have all the cards people sent to me and I treasure them. Cancer is humbling in so many ways. Learning to accept the kindness being offered to you by other people is dignifying.

It's helpful to have one person who can be your point person. Someone who is willing to send out emails updating your friends and family members on how you're doing or keep the schedule for meals. There are also numerous online resources that can help. Many people use CaringBridge or social media to update people easily and communicate information. Take Them A Meal, Meal Train or SignUpGenius are all great ways to coordinate meals.

TIP 9: GET YOUR SUPPLIES BEFORE YOU NEED THEM

If you plan to wear a wig when your hair falls out, buy it before you lose your hair. It's a hard thing to go through, and when my hair finally came out I was happy I had a wig already at my house. The last thing you're going to want to deal with is shopping for a wig when you're trying to cope with not having any hair. Trust me on this one. There are many wonderful stores with very caring and supportive people who will be happy to help you. Let them. Don't spend a ridiculous amount of money on your wig. While there are definitely different price points, I don't think it's necessary to go crazy. Buy hats, scarves and anything else you think you'll want to wear before you actually need them. Treat yourself to a new lipstick or fabulous pair of earrings. If you're a man, get an assortment of great baseball caps. A lot of people choose to rock their bald heads and don't wear any type of head covering. These people are bad asses.

Get all your prescriptions filled before you start chemo. Also, don't read the list of side effects that can occur. Instead, have a close friend or family member educate themselves so they know what to watch for. If you meet with your nurse to go over the potential side effects, which many doctors require, take a friend or family member with you so they can pay attention. I wish I had done this. I was overly focused on what was happening to my body and very uptight about what could possibly occur, but I ended up never experiencing most of the side effects I worried about. It's scary to put chemo into your body and the best thing you can do is spend your energy on taking care of yourself. Be proactive instead of re-active—this will make a huge difference in how you feel.

TIP 10: CANCER WILL ROCK THE MENTAL HEALTH OF YOU AND YOUR FAMILY

We immediately secured counselors for my daughters. They need-ed to have people they could talk to, people they were comfort-able opening up to, who could help them navigate the scary place our family was in. Even if your kids say they don't want or need to talk to a professional, make the appointment anyway. And while you're lining up counselors for your kids, you might want to find a counselor for yourself. I had weekly counseling sessions for a very long time and it was incredibly helpful. This also holds true if you're a caregiver to a loved one going through cancer. Many hospitals offer counseling services for patients and their families. Check it out. Don't forget to take care of your mind as well as your body and don't feel ashamed or weak for needing to seek counsel-ing. If it can help you, why wouldn't you want to do it?

TRIBE TIP

Don't just offer to do things to help, go ahead and do them. Instead of asking, "What can I do?" or saying, "Please let me know if you need anything," think about what you would need and just do it. Bringing ready-made healthy meals that can be put into the freezer is extremely helpful. Going to the grocery store and buying food you think might be needed is also a great way to help. Cut the grass, plant some pretty flowers or stock the pantry.

If your friend or family member has children, pick up the kids and take them for a few hours. Do something fun with them and try to distract them. Depending on their ages, take them for ice cream, Starbucks or the playground. Trust me, they'll probably welcome the opportunity to get out of their house. Kids are smart and can sense when something is going on. Helping them maintain as normal a life as possible is a great way to help your friend or loved one.

Text and send cards telling your loved one you're thinking of them. It's fine to call, but don't take it personally if they don't pick up the phone or call you back. The last thing I wanted to do was talk on the phone and have to say the same things over and over again to each person who called.

Think of it this way, your friend's life is on hold while he or she is dealing with cancer. Anything you can do to help make life easier will be greatly appreciated.

Even in the tough
seasons of life,
open your eyes and find
something to be grateful for.
It's there.
Sometimes we just
have to look a little
harder.

CHAPTER 4

CHEMO IS HARD

I was really scared about going through chemo. I was terrified about how my body would react and what would happen. We've all seen TV shows and movies that portray people having horrible side effects from chemo. I couldn't stop thinking about these scenes. I was convinced I would be one of those people.

While going through chemo was hard for me, that doesn't mean it will be hard for you. Some people sail through it and aren't even fazed. I truly hope you're one of them. In fact, I recommend you go into your chemo expecting to be one of those people. I've met people who never had to take a nausea pill or miss one day of work. This is definitely a possibility and you won't know until you get into it. If you're going through treatments now and this doesn't sound like you, don't be discouraged. I wasn't one of those people either. Partway through, I couldn't imagine going the distance with my treatment plan. I seriously thought about quitting. I'd never been through anything so difficult. While my friends were enjoying the start to their summer, talking about fun trips to the beach and travel plans, I was sitting in a chemo room, going to doctor's appointments and staying at home to avoid crowds.

I felt sorry for myself.

I felt sorry for my kids.

They didn't need a sick mom. Instead of enjoying a fun summer, they were being hit with a reality they shouldn't have had to deal with, all because of me. The guilt I carried around ran deep.

My oldest daughter was graduating from eighth grade and there was a special program at school. It was a big deal and something we had been looking forward to all year. It was a milestone I didn't want to miss. After getting the results back from my weekly blood work and learning my counts were very low, I realized I couldn't attend the program. I was devastated. How could I miss my daughter's big moment? It was hard for my daughter too, which made it even worse. It was a reminder our lives had changed and we couldn't do anything about it. Instead of attending the program, I stayed in bed, binge-watching episodes of "Mad Men," eating popsicles and crying as friends sent me pictures of the assembly. I kept thinking about how much my life had changed in such a short amount of time. I was a full-blown cancer patient and it sucked, for me and for my family. I wanted my old life back.

My family pulled together and they were glad to help. It was a true blessing they were willing to take the time to come when we needed them most. My father and stepmother came to stay at my house every week I had chemotherapy. They made sure my kids were OK, took care of the house and tried to keep things as normal as possible. Fortunately, they were retired and able and willing to do it. They would drive four hours every other week, stay at my house, take me to chemo, help out for a few days and turn around and drive home, only to do it again a week later.

Not only would they take over the house, they would attempt to manage my attitude. I wasn't exactly a ray of sunshine, and I'm sure they didn't always look forward to these visits. At one point, after dealing with me for weeks, they were fed up with me sulking, feeling sorry for myself and my anything-but-pleasant disposition. My negativity caused my father to coin the term, "emotionally efficient."

"You're spending a lot of time and energy worrying and being neg-ative. You aren't helping yourself," he said. "In fact, you're making life a lot harder than it needs to be. Open your eyes to how lucky you are. Things could be a lot worse. Instead of moping around, you need to be emotionally efficient."

I've always thought my dad was the smartest man alive, but this confirmed it. He told me what I needed to hear, even though I didn't want to. He and my stepmother encouraged me to stop wasting my emotional energy on "what ifs," guilt and things I couldn't control, and to focus instead on getting better and taking care of myself, mentally and physically. I didn't change overnight, but I started working on my attitude. I tried to be more positive. I committed to helping myself instead of making my life miserable.

After each treatment, your doctor will probably want you to come into the office to get your blood drawn to monitor how the chemo is impacting your body, as well as your risk for potential complica-tions. Your doctor will pay close attention to your white blood cell count, red blood cell count and platelet count (among other things) because these can be lowered by the drugs being administered, which can decrease your ability to fight off infections and illnesses. Don't be alarmed if you have a low blood cell count, it's very common. Almost every time they checked mine, my white blood cell count came back low. This would suck because it meant I needed to be extra careful and avoid crowds. I didn't want to get sick and have to delay my treatments. If your counts get too low, you will also more than likely feel very tired. Your doctor will give you a list of rules to follow when this happens. Follow them.

I received a lot of beautiful flowers from friends and family during chemo, and our house looked like someone had died. While I appreciated the kindness and generosity, every time the doorbell rang and a beautiful flower arrangement or plant arrived, I was reminded of being sick. I didn't realize my kids were feeling this way too until the school guidance counselor emailed me and told me my youngest daughter couldn't handle the flowers. They reminded her of a funeral parlor and she was having a very hard time with it. I gave a lot of the flowers away and tried to limit the amount coming into the house. I didn't want to seem ungrateful, but when my doorbell rang with yet another flower delivery, I almost wanted to turn them away. I didn't know what exactly we needed to get us through this, but it wasn't flowers.

I didn't work when I was going through treatment. In fact, from the day I heard the words, "You have cancer," until I was finished with all my treatment, I was out on sick leave. For me, this was an appropriate decision and one I felt very blessed to be able to make. It was challenging enough to just get through the day, I wouldn't have been very productive at work. However, many people are able to continue working while going through treatment and they are truly amazing. This is an individual decision and you must do what works for you and your family situation.

If you're able to work throughout your treatment, remember to be good to yourself. You're going to be very tired and you probably aren't going to be able to do all you're used to doing. Give yourself a break. Try to lighten your work load, reduce work-related stress and consider scheduling your chemo on a Friday so you can have the weekend to recover. Don't be surprised if you aren't able to work at your normal level of production. If you usually travel for work, think about cutting back. If you work around children or are a caregiver, you will have to be very careful because you don't want to get sick. Remember, your long-term health and staying on your treatment plan is what truly matters.

TIP 11: WHAT TO TAKE TO CHEMO

Here are 10 items you should take to the chemo room:

1. A good attitude – You don't want to be in this situation, but here's the thing, you are. You need to have a good attitude. I know it's hard, but try.

2. Layers of comfy clothing – The room will probably be very cold, kind of like an airplane (Maybe you could pretend you're on an airplane going somewhere fun? Think of the chemotherapy chair like sitting in first class.). Even if it's summertime, make sure you bring a sweater or jacket. The chemo can change your body temperature, so being able to shed a layer or put one on is helpful. Warm blankets will be offered and I highly recommend getting one, or many.

3. Warm socks – I always took my shoes off, snuggled under the warm blankets the hospital provided and put on cozy socks. Wear shoes you can slide into easily in case you have to go to the bathroom, which you will probably need to do. During chemo, a ton of liquids are pumped into your body and they're going to have to come out eventually.

4. Something to keep you busy – Take your journal, knitting, crocheting, adult coloring books, crossword puzzles, reading material or whatever else inspires you or holds your attention. The key is to try to distract yourself. Do not focus on any of the side effects I told you not to think about. The nurses will watch you closely, and should you have a reaction, which probably won't happen, they'll know exactly what to do. If you start to feel strange or something seems off, don't hesitate to tell your nurse, but don't sit in the chair and worry.

5. Chapstick – Or something to put on your lips.

6. Snacks – Bring snacks such as crackers, bananas, sliced apples, applesauce, healthy muffins or breads. Don't eat anything rich or bring foods with a strong smell. I also wouldn't recommend foods that are too sugary. Don't let your stomach get empty but don't eat too much either. It's kind of like being pregnant. Except it's not. Peanut butter crackers became my best friend.

7. Technology – It's nice to have earphones and your device so you can listen to music or podcasts or even watch a movie. Ask about Wi-Fi before you start chemo. You might not have access.

8. Something to drink – Take a large cup with either water or hot tea. I always took a large Swell bottle with my favorite tea. This worked great because it would stay warm during my entire treatment. I was usually cold, and having a warm drink was sooth-ing. While your hospital will probably offer water and other drinks, it's nice to have a large cup so you don't have to keep getting re-fills. Make sure you drink a lot, even if you aren't thirsty.

9. Mints – Or hard candy, especially peppermint.

10. Eyewear – Don't forget your glasses. If you wear contacts, you might want to take them out if you get tired (you will get tired) and want to sleep (you will want to sleep). Your glasses will enable you to see when you wake up from your nap. If, or should I say when, the drugs they administer to manage the side effects of chemo make you feel sleepy, don't fight it. Let yourself sleep. The time will pass by faster.

TIP 12: IT'S OK TO CURSE LIKE A SAILOR

I didn't grow up in a household where we used a lot of bad words. Occasionally my parents might have said "dammit," or even an oc-casional "shit," but that was only when they got overly frustrated. We knew our parents were really mad at us when we drove them to use a G-rated swear word. The F-word was never uttered. Ever.

For some reason, cancer brought out the bad words in me. It was like the door had been unlocked and my swearing was unleashed. And not just the little bad words, the big bad words. Saying "fuck" made me feel good, really good. I started using it a lot and I didn't hold back. If I had a dollar for every time I said the word "fuck" during my treatment, we'd probably be able to fund our kids' college educations. Try it. You'll see what I'm talking about. You can even scream "Fuck cancer!" and it will bring you joy. (I did have a conversation with my kids and explained they shouldn't say the F-word at school. I didn't want to get a call from the principal. Fortunately, they understood the importance of only using bad words in the house.) I even managed to frustrate my dad so much with my negative attitude he actually used the F-word one day. It was a one-time thing and hasn't happened since. I have to admit, when he said it I stopped rambling on about whatever I happened to be complaining about at the time and smiled. I had pushed my dad to the edge.

TRIBE TIP

It's no fun sitting outside the chemo room waiting for your name to be called. It's scary. If you can, offer to take your friend or family member to their treatments. Depending on the type of chemo they're getting, it could take several hours. Each time I had chemo, I would get my blood work done, meet with my doctor and then have chemo. It took a long time. If the hospital was really busy, it could take over six hours. It was very helpful to have my husband, in-laws, brother-in-law, friends or parents take me to chemo. Most of the time I slept because of the drugs, but it was nice to have someone there to talk to and distract me when I was awake.

Take something to keep you occupied when your friend or family member falls asleep. While you're at it, bring something for the person you're supporting as well. A new magazine or book can be a welcome distraction. Also, make sure you bring snacks and drinks for yourself. Just don't bring anything that has a strong smell, as people receiving chemo don't want to smell your food.

Real beauty
comes from being
a kind and
caring person.
Not a dress size or
hairstyle.

CHAPTER 5

LOSING YOUR HAIR SUCKS

After my first treatment, I thought I had this chemo thing in the bag. I took the nausea medicine and it was working. I was embracing the pharmaceutical industry and had a chart so I could remember when to take which drug. Before cancer, I would think twice about just taking an Advil. If you're like me and you don't like taking medicine, you'll quickly realize you might need to ditch this attitude.

My hair hadn't changed at all and I was even regretting the fact that I had cut it short. Besides feeling tired, life felt relatively normal. Unfortunately, the effects of chemo are cumulative. What this means is that as you receive more treatments, the drugs build up and get harder and harder on your body. Your first round will be the easiest in terms of side effects, then they will most likely get worse from there. Sorry to be the one to tell you this, but it's something you need to know. The same can be said about radiation. As you do more treatments, the impact on your skin will increase and you'll be more tired.

It only took two rounds of chemo for me to realize I was wrong about sailing through. It turns out it was going to be a little harder than I thought because I hadn't considered the emotional impact the chemo would have on me. OK, a lot harder. It was clear my hair was going to fall out. I had strands all over my pillowcase and on the floor in the shower. When I ran my hand through my hair, a huge chunk would come out.

Before I started losing my hair, I still looked the same and our lives hadn't really changed. I bounced back relatively quickly after surgery and went to chemo while my kids were at school and busy with their normal routines. But when my hair started falling out, the reality of the situation hit me. There was no denying what was going on. I couldn't pretend life was normal because it wasn't—I was dealing with cancer. I was depressed, could hardly eat and felt sick every time I looked in the mirror. I didn't feel like doing anything or going anywhere. Sensing I needed an intervention, my husband called several of my friends who came over with ice cream, wine and love. They did their best to cheer me up and pull me through, but they couldn't change the situation.

I found out my kids were crying behind closed doors with my husband because seeing my hair fall out and watching me get so upset about it was devastating to them. They started sleeping together at night and clung to each other. Knowing my kids were so upset cut me to the core. Looking back on it, I could have handled things differently. Instead of feeling sorry for myself and wallowing in my depression, I should have looked at the big picture and kept my perspective. Sometimes, it's hard to see clearly when you're in the middle of something. It's easy for me to look back now and see what I could have done to help myself. At the time, I was so caught up in feeling yucky and sorry for myself I wasn't able to help myself. This is why I'm sharing all of this with you now. If you're feeling depressed and physically sick, try to keep things in perspective. Remember, you won't always feel this way. It's temporary. Don't make things worse for yourself. Figure out what you can do to make yourself feel better and do it.

It was obvious what needed to happen. It was time to shave off what remained of my hair. Since I had cut it short already, it wouldn't take very long. My hairdresser came over to my house and together, in my bathroom, we watched as my remaining locks fell to the floor. I looked in the mirror and saw a sick person staring back at me. I didn't know who that woman was or where the real me had gone. Reality set in and it wasn't pretty. While I had a fancy wig I could wear, I didn't want to. There was no denying it, I was a full-blown cancer patient, whether I wanted to be or not.

Nothing will prepare you for losing your hair. You can read about it and talk with other people who have gone through it, but when you touch your hair and clumps fall out, it's really, really hard. I can't tell you how many people I've spoken to who tell me this was one of the worst parts of their cancer journey. We can say, "It's just hair, it'll grow back." But while we know it's true, seeing yourself bald is unimaginable until it happens. That being said, I would never not do the treatments I needed because of my hair. I'm incredibly grateful for the chemo and all the research that's been done to provide the available treatments.

While it's depressing to look in the mirror and be bald, it's what your baldness stands for that makes it so devastating. Before I lost my hair, I didn't look sick. After I shaved my head, I looked exactly like someone who was receiving treatment for cancer, which I was. My problem? I didn't want to be a cancer patient and I didn't know what to do about it. I didn't know how to look at my reflection and accept myself for who I was. I had to learn how to do this and you will too. It took time for me to get used to my new look and to figure out what I was comfortable wearing. At first I would wear a baseball cap around the house. I didn't want my kids to see me without hair because I knew it upset them and was a constant reminder their mom had cancer and wasn't immortal. I didn't know it then, but this would be the beginning of a long struggle for my kids regarding their acceptance of the uncertainty of life.

As I put on my baseball cap each morning, I'd ask my husband, "If you saw me and didn't know anything about me, would you be able to tell I don't have hair? Is it obvious, or does it just look like I have really short hair?"

Jon couldn't have been more supportive, but he wouldn't lie to me. "You can tell you don't have hair," he would say, "But why does it matter? It'll grow back."

He was right, it was obvious. He was sweet about trying to make me feel good about how I looked, saying, "I kind of like your bald chick look," or "You're rocking it."

I didn't feel like I was rocking anything. In fact, I was utterly embarrassed. I didn't want anyone to know what I was going through.

I decided to start wearing my wig. My hairdresser cut and colored it to look as natural as possible, and I wore it when I went out to meet a friend for lunch or run errands. It felt awkward at first, but I got used to it. When I wore the wig, I felt like I didn't stand out. I felt normal. When I wore a baseball cap around town, I felt like people were staring at me. I saw the looks of pity on their faces and I didn't like it. Strangers would ask me questions about my health, and I didn't want to talk about cancer all the time, especially with people I didn't know. But when I put on the wig, I could go about my business without having to talk about what I was going through, without strangers knowing what I was dealing with. I would just wear a baseball cap to my doctor's appointments at the hospital because everyone else there was dealing with cancer too.

Everyone has to figure out what works for them. Wigs are hot, especially in the summer, and baseball caps can give you a headache after wearing them for a long time. Some people like wearing scarves, but I didn't. You might just say "Screw it," and rock your beautiful bald head. You have to figure out what works for you and do what you're comfortable with. The good news is it really is just hair and it will grow back. I promise.

As time passed, I stopped focusing on my hair. I would walk around my house sporting my bald head and I didn't care. I would let friends and family and even my kids' friends see me bald. The more I grew through my experience the less important my hair seemed.

In fact, after I was finished with all of my treatments, even though I was still almost completely bald, I decided to ditch it all. I donated the wig, put away all the hats and was ready to show the world what I had earned. I had fought hard and been through a lot and I was proud of myself for what I had accomplished.

Our society places too great an importance on external appearances. I admit, I used to do the same. But not anymore. Before cancer, I was overly focused on my external appearance, evidenced by the way I acted when my hair fell out. I cared how other people saw me. Going through this humbling experience taught me how unimportant looks are. I stopped judging other people by what they looked like and started really seeing people for who they are on the inside. I know now what truly matters, and it's not the length of a person's hair.

You will probably become a more compassionate person after going through your journey and you will know, first-hand, how beauty fades and looks change, but the goodness and kindness of a person remains. The qualities on the inside are truly all that matter.

Once you lose your hair and it grows back, don't be surprised if you don't care as much about your hair or you reduce the amount of time you're willing to spend on it. It takes hair to have a bad hair day and you're going to be so happy you have hair you probably won't ever complain about it again. While I used to spend a lot of time flat-ironing my hair and getting it professionally straightened, I don't do that now. I have too many other things I'd rather be doing. It's called perspective, and after you go through cancer, you'll have it too.

TIP 13: IT'S NOT JUST THE HAIR ON YOUR HEAD THAT WILL FALL OUT

You're going to lose hair all over your body. Not just on your head. My eyebrows thinned significantly but I could fill them in with a little brown eye shadow. Eyelashes were a different story. One day I was taking a walk and bugs started hitting my eyes. I couldn't understand why until I realized I didn't have any eyelashes. This didn't happen until later in my treatment, and by then I had stopped caring as much. I didn't even consider wearing fake eyelashes, it just didn't matter to me. I also lost all the hair down there, on my vajayjay. Yep, it will happen—just part of the super fun journey. There were a few benefits: I didn't have to shave my legs, I saved money on hair products and I could get dressed and ready to leave the house in under 15 minutes.

TRIBE TIP

Give compliments when you can. Understand how difficult it is not only to get cancer and go through treatment, but also to deal with changes in appearance. This all happens quickly and it can be hard to process. It's a constant reminder each time your loved one looks in the mirror that they have cancer. Be supportive during this hard time and do everything you can to help them remember it's just hair. It will grow back. Nice gifts you might consider giving to your friend or loved one are baseball caps, earrings, scarves or a pretty lipstick.

I don't think we meet people
by accident.
**They come into our lives
for a reason.**
To teach us a lesson
or be there for us when
we need them the most.

CHAPTER 6

THE GIRL IN THE WAITING ROOM

I've always believed people come into our lives for a reason. Sometimes I can't see the lesson I'm meant to learn from a person who crosses my path right away, but when I look back on my life, there have definitely been times a random meeting with a person impacted me in a big way. This is how I feel about an interaction I had in the waiting room at the cancer center. A seemingly chance encounter with a girl that ended up being a game-changer for me. She had no idea what she did for me, and I didn't know at the time how much things would change for me after I spoke to her.

I had gotten dehydrated because I wasn't drinking enough (which is why you need to listen to me when I tell you about drinking and eating in Chapter 7) and was sitting in the hospital waiting room, a place I seemed to spend a lot of time in. I had had about enough of this cancer stuff. As I sat there feeling yucky and sorry for myself, I noticed a beautiful girl who looked to be in her 20s. She didn't seem like a cancer patient. I was bald and pale and she was the poster child of health, tanned with long hair. I couldn't stop staring at her as I tried to figure out why she was there. I had to know. Plus, it gave me something to think about besides myself.

It was just the two of us sitting in the huge room. I had been spending so much time at home I was looking forward to having a conversation with someone other than my family, even if it was a random stranger in the cancer center waiting room. (If you had told me there would be a time in my life when going to a cancer center would be the highlight of my day, I wouldn't have believed you.)

"I hope you don't mind me asking you this," I finally said to her, "but you look too healthy to be in this room. What are you here for?"

She smiled as she responded and didn't seem to mind my question.

"Oh, I'm here to meet with my doctor. Two years ago, I was diagnosed with breast cancer."

"You were? That's what I'm being treated for right now. Did you go through chemo?"

I wanted her to say yes. I wanted her to tell me she had once been in my shoes, and two years later she was doing great. I wanted her to tell me I would get through this difficult time in my life and it would be worth it. That she understood how I was feeling, had been there herself and was now on the other side of the challenging journey.

"No," she said, and paused. "My doctors wanted me to do chemo since my cancer was really aggressive, but I just couldn't stand the thought of losing my hair. I had a lumpectomy and did radiation, and I'm supposed to take medicine, but I don't. I don't like the way it makes me feel." She laughed as she said this and continued, "I don't have a death wish if that's what you're thinking. I'm eating healthy and I'm sure I'll be fine. I'm just here for my checkup. The doctor will probably yell at me for not taking the medication."

I didn't know what to say, her comments completely caught me off guard. I just smiled and we stopped talking. Her name was called a few minutes later and I found myself sitting in the waiting room by myself. That was the only time I was ever there alone. It was just me and my thoughts as I processed what she told me.

Her attitude toward cancer had thrown me. I couldn't believe she had refused to do the recommended treatment and she seemed so nonchalant about everything. From that moment on, I decided to change my attitude. I couldn't control how the treatment would make me feel. I couldn't control if I would get sick. I couldn't make my hair grow back. And suddenly none of that really mattered. What I could do, what was more important than anything else, was that I could control my attitude. I could try to be positive. I decided I would embrace my decision to be as aggressive as possible, and I wasn't going to look at chemo as something I dreaded, but rather as something I was doing to save my life. Chemo was my friend, cancer was the enemy. I needed to come to this realization. I might feel sick. I might be tired. But I was doing it. One day at a time, one treatment at a time, I was getting through it.

Talking with the girl in the waiting room that day made a huge difference for me and I want you to learn from my experience. Decide right now to be positive, regardless of what you're dealing with or where you are in your journey. Decide right now to put a smile on your face, take care of yourself and do whatever you can do to help yourself get through your treatment plan. Being negative won't do anything but make you feel bad.

Don't make things harder for yourself.

It's hard enough.

Help yourself by being emotionally efficient. Do whatever it takes to make yourself look at things in a more positive manner. Take walks, play games, do puzzles, watch TV, spend time with friends, eat healthy foods, rest. Figure out what makes you happy and do it. A lot. Even if you're tired, force yourself to do something you love each day. Something each day that helps you feel like your "normal" self. It doesn't matter what it is. Life goes on and you want to make the most of every day. I wish I had come to this realization earlier in my journey because I could have saved myself a lot of trouble and anxiety. When you find yourself going down the negative path, remember this story and the girl in the waiting room.

I never saw her again and have no idea what her name was or how she's doing. I will always believe she came into my life that day to teach me a lesson. Maybe you can learn from her too.

TIP 14: MAKE FRIENDS WITH OTHER PATIENTS

There will be lots of opportunities to meet other patients who are going through what you are. You tend to see the same people in the hospital because you stay on the same treatment schedule.

For example, if you start receiving your chemo on a Monday, you will probably stick with Mondays for all of your treatments, as will all the other patients who started that day. The same holds true for radiation. You will probably see the same people because you will be scheduled at the same time every day.

Don't be afraid to talk to other patients. Be friendly. I joined a couple breast cancer support groups and connected with a few patients. I also had two sorority sisters who were going through breast cancer at the same time I was. It was nice to be able to talk with someone who understood what I was going through and to share tips and helpful hints.

There are lessons to learn when you're in the chemo room or the waiting room at your doctor's office. You will see people who are in worse shape than you and people who are facing better circumstances. It doesn't matter. Don't compare yourself to other people or their situation. Do the best you can with the hand you've been dealt, put a smile on your face and manage your attitude. A lot of the people you meet will finish their treatments and go into remission. They will move on with their lives and put cancer behind them. There will also be patients who don't make it. Remember these people.

TIP 15: GERMS

Limit your exposure to crowds and people who are sick. Instead of going to shopping centers or malls, try to order what you need online. Many grocery stores have delivery or pick-up services. If you go to religious services, don't hug everyone you see. People will be excited to see you and everyone will probably want to come up and hug you. Don't let them. You can't risk getting sick. Keep hand sanitizer by your front door and insist that everyone who comes into your home either wash their hands or use the hand sanitizer. Do everything you can to stay healthy. If you get sick it will take your body longer to fight off the infection and it could slow down your treatment plan. If you have young kids, limit the number of their friends who come into your house. Explain to your kids the importance of covering their mouths and noses when they cough and sneeze. Kids are germ magnets, and you have to be selfish and take care of yourself. Remember, this is a short-term issue. If you have to miss events or social functions, remind yourself why you're going through chemo in the first place. It's to save your life.

TRIBE TIP

If you aren't feeling well or have been around anyone who has been sick, try to stay away from the patient. This is very important because he or she doesn't need to be exposed to anyone who is sick. Even a little cold could turn into something more serious with a low white blood cell count. If you have young kids who often bring home lots of germs, pay attention to this. You don't want to do anything that might hurt your friend or family member or prolong their treatments.

Focus on what
you can control and
**help yourself
get better.**

CHAPTER 7

MAKE SURE YOU'RE EATING

When you're fighting cancer, making sure you get the proper nutrition can be difficult. Depending on your treatment, you might have strong food aversions, cravings for foods you don't regularly eat, or you might not be hungry at all. Chemo can also make food taste differently. I had a metallic taste in my mouth that would come and go for many months and thought food tasted like cardboard. It was hard enough for me to eat at times because I felt nauseous, then when you added the change in taste, it became a huge issue. It's not uncommon for many cancer patients to start losing weight. Other people take steroids before, during and after their chemo, which makes them extremely hungry. While I did take steroids before some of my chemo treatments, it didn't really increase my appetite significantly.

It's ideal to eat as healthy as possible during your treatment and recovery, but if you're having trouble eating, give yourself a break and just eat whatever you can. This is even more important if you've been losing weight—you need the calories. If you're extremely hungry because of the steroids, make sure you eat foods that are healthy and will give your body nutrients to make you stronger. Don't eat a bunch of junk or wasted calories; instead, choose foods packed with vitamins and minerals.

I've always been the kind of person who doesn't eat when I'm nervous or upset. Getting a cancer diagnosis made me feel both. As a result, I struggled with my eating. Nothing sounded good to me so I just didn't eat. This led to me getting dehydrated. I remember my friend coming over and trying to get me to eat a yogurt. It was breakfast time but I just couldn't face food.

"How about a few bites?" my friend asked.

"I can't," I said. "I just can't do it."

Here's exactly what you need to do to prevent yourself from feeling sick from not eating: Eat regularly. Even if you aren't hungry, force yourself to eat small amounts of food. It's best to eat at least six times a day. This way you're not letting too much time go by before your next meal. You don't want to let your stomach get too empty or you'll start getting nauseous. Once this happens, it's really hard to turn it around. Trust me on this, I'm speaking from experience. It's a cycle you don't want to get in the middle of.

I figured out peanut butter crackers were my saving grace. I kept them on the nightstand by my bed. I would eat them before I got up in the morning just to have something in my stomach. I didn't want to get dehydrated again and really made a point to make sure I ate and drank regularly.

Don't be surprised if you crave foods you don't usually eat. I had a huge craving for mashed potatoes. I remember a friend calling me one day, someone who was bringing me dinner, and she asked me what I wanted.

"If you brought me mashed potatoes, I would think you're a rock star," I said.

She brought me a huge container of mashed potatoes and it's all I ate for a couple of days. While I like mashed potatoes, it isn't something I eat regularly. But, that's what I wanted. Other foods I craved were lime popsicles and cheese pizza.

If you really can't eat regularly, at least force yourself to drink fluids all day long. Drink water, hot tea, ginger ale, juice or whatever works for you. Stay hydrated. Carry a water bottle with you at all times and sip on it. Even if you aren't thirsty, force yourself to take sips. This is especially important when you're getting chemo. I would try to drink a lot the day before my treatment and then for the next few days after. You want to get the chemo out of your system, and the best way to do this is to drink a lot of fluids. There are many drinks that provide nutrients and a larger quantity of calories. You can even order these online if you don't want to go to the grocery store. I spent a lot of time talking with the employees at Whole Foods who helped me find some meal replacement drinks that were healthy and provided me with extra calories.

Once I committed to eating six times a day, I started to feel much better. I was able to focus more on eating foods that provided my body with the nutrients it needed instead of the foods I craved. I didn't go anywhere without taking a couple snacks with me, just in case I started to feel like I needed to eat. I usually had crackers or cut-up fruit, or both, in my purse.

I'm a huge believer in smoothies and try to have a green smoothie each day. You can mix frozen berries or fruit in with spinach or kale as well as peanut butter, almonds, chia seeds or protein powder. The options are endless. Experiment until you find something you like. This is a great way to get the calories and nutrition you need. If you're having a hard time eating because you're just not hungry, drinking your nutrients and calories can be a good option.

If your white blood cell count gets really low, you might be instructed to eat only cooked fruits and vegetables. If this happens, try to get your nutrients from different types of cooked vegetables. Soup can be a huge help if this happens. You'll be able to take in the vegetables you need without having to eat a lot of food.

Try looking at food as a form of medicine. On the days I ate only popsicles I wasn't getting the nutrients I needed, but at least I was taking in calories and staying hydrated. Many hospitals have nutritionists who specialize in helping cancer patients get their needed nutrition. Some will visit you in the chemo room while you're getting your treatment. Ask your doctor about this service and take advantage of it.

Now that I'm on the other side of cancer, I eat as healthy as I can. I try to eat organic food and limit processed products. I eat a lot of fruits, vegetables, grains, nuts and beans. I make sure my meat sources are lean, organic and raised without antibiotics. It's more expensive to eat this way, but it's important to me. I have a green smoothie almost every day and try to make it with more vegetables than fruit. A few times a week I drink fresh green juice made from organic produce. I watch the amount of sugar I eat. While I'm addicted to dark chocolate, I limit myself to a few squares each day. It's my treat and it makes me happy. I will absolutely allow myself permission to eat dessert if it's a special occasion or if we happen to be somewhere and I love what is being served. However, I don't eat sweets every day, besides the dark chocolate that is organic and high in cocoa. I rarely drink alcohol and drink a lot of filtered water and green tea instead. The benefits of green tea are huge and it's something I've always liked.

I still eat six times a day, and my snacks tend to be vegetable focused. Carrots and hummus, leftover vegetables from the night before, organic celery with almond butter. I enjoy going out with my family, but try to select healthy choices from the menu. Most of the time I order wild-caught fish or eat vegetarian with whatever vegetables happen to be available. I still eat pizza every now and then and will indulge in french fries if we're going to a restaurant where I happen to like them. Fast food isn't something I eat often. If I meet a friend for coffee, I'll order a cappuccino with organic milk or almond or coconut milk. If they don't have any of those options, I'll usually get a hot cup of tea. I don't drink sugary coffees, ever, or use artificial sweeteners. I'd much rather have real food.

I try to eat probiotics in the form of plain organic Greek yogurt or sauerkraut. I also take a daily probiotic. Since I eat a lot of foods that can produce gas, this helps me. Sorry if that's too much information—I'm just keeping it real! (Remember, I promised not to withhold any information in this book.)

TIP 16: EATING DURING CHEMO

The night before chemo, I would recommend eating a light, healthy meal. Take a pass on a huge feast and instead go with something simple. I found that eating an egg and toast for dinner the evening after I received chemo helped me the most. It was light and full of protein. I almost always ate this before I went to bed. Get someone to make it for you, as you probably won't want to do it yourself. Whatever you do, don't eat your favorite foods immediately after receiving chemo. I still can't eat the soup I used to love from one of my favorite restaurants because it didn't sit well with me after one of my treatments. Huge bummer.

Of course, everyone is different and receiving different kinds of chemo. Figure out what works for you and stick with it. Don't be hard on yourself if you can't eat the foods you're used to eating, you don't have much of an appetite or you aren't able to eat as healthy as you'd like. The important thing is that you eat often, whatever works for you, and you don't let yourself get sick or lose too much weight from not eating. After you complete your treatment you'll be able to focus more on eating for nutrition.

TRIBE TIP

It can be challenging for someone who hasn't gone through chemo to understand how difficult it can be for a patient to eat. If you're caring for someone who isn't eating well, try to offer small amounts of food more frequently. Experiment with a variety of foods until you find what works. Everyone is different. Some of the foods I found easiest to eat were baked potatoes, mashed potatoes, eggs, popsicles, soup, applesauce, ice cream, yogurt and oatmeal. Don't get frustrated with the cancer patient you're helping. He or she isn't trying to be difficult, it's just really hard to eat sometimes. If you've signed up to bring a meal to your friend or family member, you might want to check in before making it. That way you can make sure you bring something they want to eat.

It's hard to understand why
bad things happen.
**Especially when it doesn't
make any sense.**
You just have to hold
onto faith and trust
there's a bigger plan.

CHAPTER 8

A WEEKEND AT THE HOSPITAL

I was getting through the journey one day at a time, one treatment at a time. I just wanted to be done with all of this cancer stuff. I felt like my life consisted of doctors' appointments and taking pills. I couldn't wait for the summer to pass, and it felt like it was moving at a snail's pace. My life was on hold. While I tried to live in the present moment and enjoy the here and now, it was hard when my appointment book didn't have anything in it but getting blood work done, doing chemo and seeing my many doctors.

The days were long.

The weeks passed slowly.

The months seemed to take forever.

My treatment consisted of a total of eight infusions, four of one kind of chemo and four of another. I received it every other week for a total of four months. I was almost done with the first half of treatments and thrilled to finally have my fourth and last round of a concoction the color of red Kool-aid, otherwise known as "the red devil." It earned the name honestly because it makes you feel like you've swallowed Satan himself. It looks like something that should be mixed with vodka and called an "afternoon delight," but it's anything but delightful. I still have trouble drinking anything red and I'm not sure I'll ever find a red beverage enticing again. Fortunately, I was never a fan of vodka and cranberry juice.

My first three treatments had gone well, but I was popping nausea pills every six or eight hours. They were causing some minor side effects, so I decided to try a different nausea medication.

This was a really bad idea.

After the fourth round of chemo, I started vomiting several hours after receiving it. I never knew I could feel so badly and it's not something I ever want to forget. It's a memory that keeps me grounded and compassionate. When I'm having a hard day or complaining about something insignificant, all I have to do is close my eyes and remember that weekend in July. The weekend I spent feeling sick and sorry for myself. The weekend I ended up in the hospital.

After a few torturous hours and conversations with my doctor's office, to the emergency room we went. I was wearing my PJs and sporting a baseball cap. Even though it was July, I was freezing. I had on a ski jacket and thick wool socks. I was holding a large plastic bin to throw up in, a cup filled with mouthwash and a washcloth to wipe my mouth. What can I say? I'm an organized sick person.

It was pitiful.

My husband dropped me off at the entrance and went to park the car. I walked up to the registration desk, put my bin filled with vomit on the counter and said I needed help. The girl working at the desk took one look at me and my bin and said, "Go stand over there and we'll get to you as quickly as possible."

Everyone in the room was looking at me but I didn't care. I just wanted to curl up into a ball on the floor and die. You know when you feel so terrible you just want someone to put you out of your misery? In that moment, I was the person everyone felt sorry for. I had never been that person and it was one of the most humbling moments of my life.

Remember how I told you going through a cancer diagnosis is a humbling experience? You're stripped down to your very soul and everything is exposed. I couldn't hide behind my before-cancer appearance. I couldn't pretend this wasn't happening to me. Looking back on it, in some ways I wish everyone could experience what I did that day. It's not that I want people to feel sick, not at all. But think how kind and caring the world would be if everyone knew how hard life is for some people. It's easy for people to take what they have for granted when everything is going well because they don't realize how difficult life can get. Once you go through an incredibly challenging experience and you survive, you will be changed forever. Standing in the ER holding my own vomit was one of those experiences.

"Please help me," I said to the doctor who was assigned to me. "I need drugs. Now."

Fortunately, there are many amazing drugs that work quickly. After I felt marginally better, they admitted me. My room was on the cancer floor. This is a place where a lot of very sick patients stay. Some people were recovering from surgery, some were at the advanced stages of the disease and other patients were experiencing side effects from the disease or treatments or were fighting an infection. The people who work on a hospital oncology floor are some of the kindest, most compassionate people I've ever met. Being on the cancer floor of a hospital provides a glimpse of how hard life can be. Most of us walk through our days not thinking about the cancer floor of a hospital or what other people are facing. We don't go there in our minds because we don't want to.

Even though I knew I was one of the healthiest people staying on the cancer floor, it was still a hard place to be. My daughters would visit me and it was scary for them. There I was, skinny and bald, wearing a hospital gown, attached to an IV. When we walked, I would push the IV pole with one hand and one of my daughters would hold my other hand. I could see the fear in their eyes and it broke my heart. I felt guilty for making them see this. This was not how my life was supposed to go. Why were my kids having to come to a cancer floor instead of the beach?

I sailed through the last four chemo treatments with my original nausea medication. I learned my lesson about changing prescriptions in the hopes of finding something better and just dealt with the minor side effects from the drug that worked for me. I wasn't going to do anything voluntarily that might send me back to the hospital.

At my last chemo treatment, the girl I was seated next to turned to me and congratulated me on being done.

"When will you be finished?" I asked her. Her answer reminded me how lucky I was.

"I'll never be done," she said. "I'll be taking some form of chemo for the rest of my life."

TIP 17: STICK TO WHAT WORKS

When you figure out a regimen that works for you, don't change it. Are you listening to me? DO NOT MESS WITH WHAT IS WORKING! I did really well with my first three treatments and should have stayed the course. You might have to experiment with different medicines and routines to help figure out what works for you, but once you find it, don't change it. The reason I got so sick after my fourth chemo was probably because I changed my medications. Learn from me. Establish a plan that works and stick to it.

If you make the decision to go through chemo, embrace your decision. View it as medicine you are proactively taking that will help you. After all, that's what it is. It's hard to walk into the chemo room and willingly allow your body to be injected with something that can cause you to feel badly, but it doesn't do any good to be negative about what you're going through. Expect good things to happen. Expect the chemo to work. Expect to feel OK after getting it. Have faith in the doctors and nurses and in the medication they give you. The drugs that are available to manage the side effects of chemo are amazing. We're lucky to have them. Take them.

TIP 18: EVERY TIME YOU DRIVE PAST A HOSPITAL

Have you ever driven past a hospital and really thought about what was going on inside? What the patients there are facing? Before my experience, I have to admit, I hadn't given it a lot of thought. Here's the thing, there isn't a lot separating the people on the outside of the hospital from those who are forced to stay inside, except for good, old-fashioned luck. I used to drive by a hospital many times in a given week without even once thinking I could be one of the sick people who were staying there. That all changed the weekend I was a patient. It was an incredibly humbling moment and one I will never forget.

Whenever I drive past a hospital now, I always say a little prayer for all the people who are inside. I encourage you to do the same. Don't ever forget how lucky you are to be on the outside. No matter what you're facing or going through, it could always be worse. Remember this. And, if you happen to be reading this from a hospital bed, have faith in your doctors and medical care, try to keep a positive attitude and remember there are a lot of people in your corner, cheering you on and hoping you're going to feel better soon.

TRIBE TIP

Even after the patient is done with treatments, he or she is probably still going to be exhausted. Don't assume they no longer need help because the treatment plan is finished. Also, just because the treatments are over doesn't mean the person will be able to walk away from cancer. There will always be doctor's appointments, blood work and even scans. Once you get diagnosed with the "Big C" it's always there, even if it's just an annual checkup. It will take many years before the doctor visits stop, if they ever do.

I'm moving forward.
One day at a time,
one step at a time.
It might be hard,
but I'm going to keep on
keeping on.

CHAPTER 9

RADIATION IS A DAILY GIG

Since there had been a microscopic-sized met in my sentinel node—the lymph node they use to see if the cancer has spread to your lymphatic system—radiation was recommended. I decided I'd gone this far I may as well do it all. I wanted to be able to look back and feel like I had done everything I could to give myself the best possible outcome. I had a lot to live for and I wasn't ready to cash in my chips.

After chemo, I took a couple weeks off, per my doctors' orders, before moving forward with radiation. I met with my radiation oncologist and was introduced to a new group of nurses and medical personnel. The thing about radiation is that it's a daily gig. What this means is that you're thinking about cancer every single day. Even if you don't want to be thinking about it, and you've made peace with your cancer and are starting to move on, the actual act of driving to the hospital and waiting for your appointment will remind you that you are still a cancer patient.

I did 30 treatments—Monday through Friday for six weeks. I think now there are different options where you can receive a higher dose in a shorter amount of time. It's amazing to see the advancements medicine has made even since I went through my treatment. Regardless of the schedule decided on by your doctors, you have to follow certain rules when going through radiation.

You can't skip an appointment, and believe me, it's inconvenient to have to be at the hospital five days a week at a specific time. The hospital will make a schedule for you and expect you to be at your appointment at the designated time. This is very important because there are a lot of people receiving radiation and only a few machines. If you're late, it messes up the schedule for all the other patients that day.

At first, I would go to the hospital every day, put on a gown and wait for them to call my name. Eventually I got to the point where I would wear a shirt I could easily slip off and skip the gown. I would wait for them to call my name, go in, take my shirt off and get right on the table. I was ready to be done with all this cancer stuff. Since I wasn't getting any medication that made me tired, I was able to take myself to my appointment and didn't have to inconvenience anyone. It doesn't take very long, unlike chemo where you sit for hours at a time.

After each radiation treatment, I would go home, take a nap and try to preserve my energy for later in the day. This way I would have enough energy to be with my kids when they came home from school. Spending time with my beautiful daughters, so young and filled with promise, was a good reminder of why I was going through all of this. I wanted to live for them. I wanted to see them grow up.

Compared to chemo, radiation was a lot easier for me because it didn't make me feel sick. The worst side effects I experienced from radiation were reddening of the radiated area and fatigue. Don't be surprised if your skin gets very red or even starts to peel. It's like having a really bad sunburn that gets dry and flaky. This won't happen immediately, but rather over time, as they continue to radiate the same skin repeatedly. There are creams you can put on to relieve the burning sensation. The type of cancer you're dealing with, as well as the strength of the radiation, will impact your side effects. For example, radiation to the digestive system can cause digestive issues. Everyone is different and the side effects will vary.

The fatigue I experienced during radiation was unlike anything I'd ever felt. There's a difference between being tired and feeling fatigued. When you're tired, you want to sleep. When you try to fall asleep you're usually able to do so and it helps. There's nothing like waking up from a good night's sleep and feeling refreshed. On the other hand, when you are fatigued, you feel weak and don't have much energy. You don't have the stamina to do what you want to do. You feel exhausted, but you aren't necessarily sleepy. While it helps to take naps, if you can fall asleep, you might find when you wake up you don't feel rested.

Fatigue is a common side effect of radiation. What do you do to manage this? You take it easy and conserve your energy. You pace yourself. If there's something you really want to do during the day, plan for it.

Fortunately, when the treatments stop, you'll slowly start to gain your energy back. Several weeks after you've completed your radiation, you will start to notice you don't feel as tired. It will take time, so be patient with yourself. I got so used to taking a nap every day, it's something I still frequently do now, even if it's just 20 or 30 minutes. I like to put my feet up, close my eyes and give my body a little rest. If you've never been a napper, don't dismiss the benefits or how good it can feel.

I'm not sure my kids really even knew I was going to the hospital every day for radiation. I downplayed it because I could tell they were ready to just put this whole cancer thing behind them. And, since I felt good and was able to drive myself to the hospital for the treatments, our life started to feel somewhat normal again. My hair started growing back, I ditched the wig, got rid of all the medication I was taking during chemo and saved up my energy for my family. My health had felt like the focus of our family for so long, I craved normalcy for all of us.

After chemo, it would take a lot to faze me. If I hadn't gone through chemo, radiation might have been a bigger deal. But I had been going to the cancer center for months and had made a lot of friends, so I didn't mind. I didn't have the fear with radiation that I had with chemo. My attitude was, "I can deal with feeling fatigued. As long as my digestive system is happy, I don't care."

TIP 19: THE DAILY GIG CAN GET OLD

I know it's hard to go to the hospital every day for your treatment. It makes you feel like you have to deal with cancer every day, that cancer is taking over your life. Remember to have a positive attitude and be flexible. Don't make this harder on yourself by being negative. I used to try to plan something fun to do after radiation several times a week. Since I was already out, it was easy to meet a friend for lunch or grab a cup of tea. I even started working out a little bit while going through radiation. I was anxious to get my body back and start lifting weights again. Take it slowly though, and remember it's normal to be tired. Don't push yourself and be sure to rest when necessary.

Don't be late for your radiation appointments. The hospital staff won't like it if you mess up their schedule, and you don't want to do anything to piss them off.

When you get worn down from your treatments, remind yourself why you're doing what you're doing. If you're going through a difficult time right now, hang in there. You can get through this. It's hard to keep perspective when you don't feel good. It's especially easy to pity yourself and wonder if you will ever feel good again. More than likely you will. When you're having a bad day, take it hour by hour. Do what you can to help yourself get better. Be gentle and compassionate with yourself. Going through cancer is hard. Period.

TRIBE TIP

Understand the level of fatigue the patient is going to experience during radiation. When someone says he or she is too tired to attend an event, whatever it is, let them know you absolutely understand.

I remember my last day of radiation was the day before Halloween. I was exhausted. There was no way I was going to be able to go trick-or-treating with my kids and friends. Even though I wanted to go, it would have been really hard for me to walk that much. And I was an active person who was used to working out regularly before cancer. My point is, until you go through it, you can't understand how exhausted someone might feel.

No one said life was going
to be easy or fair.
**Do the best you can
with the hand
you've been dealt.**
Control what you can control.

CHAPTER 10

BE CAREFUL WHAT YOU WISH FOR

On the last day of my treatment, while everyone around me was congratulating me, I tried to fake a smile and be happy. But, I wasn't. I was thrilled to have the treatments behind me, but truth be told, I was scared. I made my way to the hospital chapel, a room off the hospital's main entrance, and sat there and cried. It was the first time I had gone there. I needed a place to sit alone and just be. To collect my thoughts. To let it all out. Everything I had been keeping inside me for months came pouring out. All of it.

I cried because I was happy to be done.

I cried because I felt grateful to be where I was and knew how lucky I was.

I cried for all of the people I had met along my journey who weren't as lucky as I was.

Most of all, I cried because I was terrified. If I was done with all my treatments, that meant I wasn't actively doing anything to prevent the cancer from coming back. And if I had gotten cancer once, how could I be sure it wouldn't happen again?

I felt like a sitting duck. The walls of the hospital had become my safe haven, a place to come and fight the enemy. If I left the battle-field, how could I be sure the enemy wouldn't return? When my guard was down and I had gone back to living life, how would I stay protected? I found this unsettling.

My doctor and I had discussed how often I would come in for blood work and checkups. I was scheduled to have a hysterectomy to give myself even more protection and I was about to start tak-ing a daily pill for added security. We had a plan and I had a lot going for me. I knew I was lucky and had a lot of options, but I wanted a sure thing.

Sadly, nothing is 100%. Nothing is guaranteed. My doctor couldn't look me in the eye and promise I would live to be an old lady, even though this is exactly what I wanted and needed to hear. I wanted her to pinky swear cancer wouldn't ever come knocking at my door again. She knew I wanted her to tell me this but she also knew she couldn't make that promise. Dammit.

There isn't a cancer patient out there who isn't afraid it will hap-pen again. A heart patient probably worries about having another attack. A stroke patient likely fears having another, more debilitat-ing stroke. The same holds true for cancer. It's really hard to live with, this internal struggle. Conquering the uneasiness and uncer-tainty became my next quest. I didn't know how to deal with it right then, but I was determined to eventually figure it out.

TIP 20: CONTROL WHAT YOU CAN CONTROL

Hopefully, after you complete your treatments, you will receive positive news about your success and be told to get back to living your life. If your doctor decides to add additional treatments or modify the original plan, don't fall apart. Remember, your doctor is doing everything he or she can to give you the best prognosis going forward. While I know you're probably ready to be done with the "Big C," listen to your doctors.

This is the time to focus on how to help yourself. Concentrate on what you can do to stay healthy. Eat well, exercise and make sure you strengthen your mental health by managing your stress and trying to make peace with cancer. We'll get to that more in the next section of this book, but empower yourself by focusing your energy on what you can do to take care of yourself. Completing your treatment plan is a huge milestone. Don't be surprised if it brings both positive and negative feelings. We'll talk more about this in the next section of the book too.

TIP 21: KEEP ON KEEPING ON

It's easy to feel sorry for yourself or overwhelmed with what you're facing. Don't let that get in the way of enjoying life's sacred moments. Force yourself to go out with friends, spend time doing things you've always liked doing and make a conscious effort to move forward and live. It's easy to stop being social and stay home when you're dealing with an illness, especially if you don't feel good or you're insecure about how you look.

A nurse once told me, "When you get up in the morning, brush your teeth, put on your wig and move on with your day." It was good advice for me and it is for you too.

Make sure you don't fill your calendar only with doctor's appointments and treatments. You owe it to yourself to do something that brings you joy each and every day. Try to keep your life as normal as possible, even though your life is anything but normal. Listen to your body and do what feels right, but don't be afraid to push yourself a little bit. It's easy to feel tired and down and give in to staying home and watching TV. Don't just make your life about getting through cancer. You've got to live too!

TRIBE TIP

My close friends wanted to celebrate the fact that I was done with treatment. It had been a long haul and they had stood by me each step of the way. My success was their success. But I didn't really feel like celebrating.

They wanted to throw me a party and I didn't want to go. While I knew they were just being kind, I was a mess. They wanted to honor and celebrate me and I wanted to crawl into bed and sob. What they viewed as a moment to celebrate was the moment I realized I didn't know how to live. How was I going to live each day of the rest of my life knowing that my body had failed me? Knowing there was a time when cancer was brewing inside my body and I didn't have any idea? I forced myself to put on a smile, wrote a thank-you speech and ended up having a great night. It was a reminder to me that we have to mark the good moments for what they are, take the time to celebrate joyful occasions and not let our minds get in the way of having a good time.

It's OK to push the patient to celebrate the good news and happy occasions when they come. Don't be surprised if you're met with a little resistance, but push forward. It's important to recognize the positive milestones when we have them and not let them pass by us without taking the time to celebrate them.

True friends
see you at your worst
and love you
anyway.

CHAPTER 11

YOU'LL LEARN WHO YOU CAN COUNT ON

When you get diagnosed with a serious illness, you find out who your true friends are really quickly. It's easy to be friends with someone when everything is wonderful and fun. It's a lot harder to be friends with a sick person who is vomiting and depressed. Nothing says fun like a crying bald person laced with throw-up.

Although I've always been a social person, during my treatment our social life took a back seat. When you aren't feeling good, the last thing you want to do is go to a party. Plus, it can be stressful to go out because people will want to talk about your illness and ask you questions. Throughout my treatment, I felt like a cancer magnet. It's like everyone needed to tell me about someone they knew who was going through cancer.

One evening, I was happy to be out and was having a great time at a party. Until it happened. Until the person I was talking to said these words to me:

"My friend who had cancer two years ago just found out her cancer came back and it's really bad."

In that one moment, everything stopped. I don't even remember the rest of the conversation because I could hardly breathe. The only thing I could think about from that moment on was my cancer, her friend and the fact that I didn't want what happened to her friend to happen to me. I'm sure she didn't realize how much I would be impacted by her sharing that news or how it would affect me. I found my husband and signaled to him our night on the town was over.

I learned a lot about people while on this journey. The truth is, some people let me down. People I had been friends with for a really long time weren't there for me when I needed them most. This was a huge disappointment and hard to accept. Other people, people I hardly even knew before my diagnosis, surprised me by being there when I wouldn't have expected it. I learned I had to accept people for who they are and where they were coming from.

You might notice your friends acting differently around you. Your cancer diagnosis will impact everyone in your life. Some of your friends won't be able to handle it and will drift away from you. Others will stand by you, strengthening your relationship and helping you get through one of the hardest times in your life.

I categorized people into four groups, which helped me see where everyone fit into my life while dealing with cancer. It helped me not feel hurt by the people who weren't there for me and deeply appreciate those who were. It was my way of having a little fun with something that was difficult. Here's my personal scale, laced with humor and truth. Don't be surprised if you have people in your life who fit into each of these categories:

Category 1: Your true tribe. The people you love with all your heart and expect to be there for you. These are your people. People who have seen you at your worst and love you anyway. People you would call in the middle of the night and who would be there for you at any time. Anyone in this category is dependable and trustworthy and a true blessing in your life. Don't take them for granted, ever.

Category 2: These are the people you were acquaintances with before your diagnosis. You would see these people at the grocery store and stop and talk with them, but you never did anything socially. You didn't expect them to be there for you, so it's a pleasant surprise when you find them in your corner during your cancer fight. They are kind and thoughtful. This experience will strengthen your relationship with them and you will forever be grateful to them. You will also become one of these people going forward. When you hear about someone getting a serious diagnosis or going through a difficult time, you will want to help. You'll know the kindness of people is what carried you through your journey and you'll return the favor.

Category 3: These are the people who let you down. You would have expected them to be there for you, maybe even in Category 1, but they didn't show up. They're MIA. These people looked the other way and didn't want to have anything to do with you. I have a theory about the members of this category. It took me a little while to figure it out, but I think it's spot-on. These are the people who can't handle the fact you got cancer. They couldn't deal with it, or didn't want to deal with it. If something could happen to you, that means something could happen to them. Your illness reminds them of their vulnerability.

I tried not to let myself get upset about the friends who I expected to be there for me but ended up in this category instead. It still hurt. Hopefully you won't have a lot of people in this category. Just remember, it isn't about you.

Category 4: The people in this category are the ones who talk without thinking. The people who say stupid things that hurt you. They don't mean to hurt your feelings, they just don't know what to say to you. And in an effort to say the right thing, they say something completely opposite. I was especially sensitive, so I had to remind myself no one was trying to be mean or malicious.

Some comments that stand out in my mind are:

"My friend had the same thing and she died a few years later."

"I'm terrified for your family."

"I don't know why you're going through chemo, it will give you cancer."

"I'm worried for your future."

"Your kids are so young. How awful for them."

I know these people didn't mean to hurt my feelings or upset me, but they did. I was in a fragile state and could cry at the drop of a hat. I learned to recover faster when I was out somewhere and one of these remarks would fly my way, but it took time.

TIP 22: OTHER PEOPLE ARE GOING TO DO WHAT THEY WANT TO DO

You can't control how people will react to your illness. Be grateful for the people who love and support you. Let them build you up. Feel their strength and allow them to do nice things for you. Don't get fixated on people who let you down. If someone isn't going to support you or be there for you, it doesn't matter.

Don't take the helpful people in your life for granted, especially those in Category 1. Allow yourself to be pleasantly surprised by the people in Category 2 and pay it forward. When you're able to help someone going through a difficult time, even if it's not a close friend, remember how much you appreciated the kindness other people showed you. Don't be too hard on the people in Categories 3 and 4. Some people just can't handle cancer or don't know what to say—it's not personal. Show them a little grace, and if and when they come around, consider welcoming them back into your life. Unfortunately, you've got to get used to other people saying things you don't want to hear. You have to learn to not let what other people say impact how you feel. It will take time, but you'll get there, I promise.

My cancer experience actually helped to strengthen my relationships with many people in my life. I know who is included in my tribe, who I can count on in hard times, and I won't take them for granted. Ever.

TIP 23: YOU ARE NOT SOMEONE'S STORY

People are going to share their cancer stories with you. They will tell you everything. The good, the bad and the really, really ugly you never wanted to know about. I don't know why people do this, but you've got to remember you are not these stories. Every person is different, and just because something happened to someone's friend doesn't mean the same thing will happen to you. Unfortunately, other than when I was first diagnosed, most of the stories people shared with me were negative. People didn't tell me about their friend who had cancer 15 years ago and is out living life. These are the stories I really wanted to hear. These are the stories that would encourage me and fill me with hope. There are plenty of these stories out there.

You have to learn how to deal with what other people tell you and not allow yourself to personalize the information. I came up with a standard response to use whenever someone would start to share a negative story with me. Here's what I would say:

"I'm so sorry to hear about your friend. Thanks for sharing it with me, but everyone is different and I'm doing the best I can."

Then I would either change the subject or stop talking to that person.

TRIBE TIP

You need to know that anyone who has been through cancer is sensitive to hearing about another patient having a reoccurrence. Try very hard to watch what you say. This is especially important if you hear of someone who has passed away from cancer. Don't dwell on this or bring it up over and over again to someone who is a patient or survivor. It is anxiety-provoking and doesn't help. Every time I hear of someone with breast cancer passing away or having a reoccurrence, it rocks my world. While I know there are many different kinds of breast cancer, and no one else's situation has anything to do with my diagnosis, it still hits home. Be aware of this, always.

Just like the seasons,
whatever you're going through
will pass.
**Try to enjoy the
moment you're in.**
Remember, it will soon
be a memory.

CHAPTER 12

YOU ARE WHO YOU ARE

When my mom was 52, she passed away from skin cancer. It was melanoma, the most aggressive and deadliest form. I watched her fight like hell and lose. Watching someone you love fight a losing battle is heart-wrenching and tragic. I was in my twenties when she passed away weeks after I had my first daughter, and I felt lost without her.

When I was initially on the table in the doctor's office having my biopsy done, I remember crying and feeling helpless. I sat there sobbing while a doctor performed my biopsy and I listened as he told me I needed to prepare myself. I'm sure he wondered what he did wrong to have to deal with me (He ended up giving me his cell number, something I'm sure he regrets because I'm not afraid to use it.). But I know firsthand how hard it is to be a daughter living in a world without a mom and I would never want that to happen to my two daughters.

I didn't want what happened to my mom to happen to me.

I didn't want my daughters to have to grow up without me.

I had to learn my mom's story wasn't my story.

I had to keep telling myself my mom's outcome didn't have anything to do with my diagnosis. Just because she passed away from cancer didn't mean I was going to pass away from cancer. It was challenging to remember this. I also felt guilty about my prognosis when I compared it to what she faced. Before my mom started her chemo, she was told she had approximately a 7% chance of it working. She didn't even consider not trying.

"It works for some people," I remember her telling me. "Why shouldn't I be one of the 7%? Someone has to be."

My numbers weren't anything like her numbers, and I had to constantly remind myself that her cancer wasn't my cancer.

Some cancers are hereditary. While I did every kind of genetic test available, nothing ever showed up. Many people receive a cancer diagnosis who don't have any family history of cancer. They become the first person in their family to have to deal with the "Big C." There are others whose family members were diagnosed with cancer before them, even the same type of cancer they find themselves facing. If you come from a family where cancer seems to be lurking and you're getting more from your parents than just your beautiful hair or pretty eyes, you aren't alone. My family has cancer running through it, among other things, and it isn't something I'm glad to have. But I don't have a choice. We can't control our genetic makeup. However, just because someone has a genetic predisposition to a particular illness doesn't mean they're destined to get it.

Losing my mom to skin cancer changed the way I approach spending time in the sun. I try not to be in the sun during the hours when the sun is the strongest. If I am, I make sure to wear protective clothing and sunscreen, and I usually wear a hat. If I go to the beach, I always sit under an umbrella. I've tried to educate my daughters on the importance of being smart when it comes to spending time in the sun. Most of the time they listen. I'm vigilant about going to the dermatologist and getting checked for skin cancer. I pay attention to any changes in my skin, especially any changes in the moles on my body. When I have one removed, it makes me nervous, and my dermatologist understands this because he knows what my family went through. As a result, he is wonderful about getting my test results back quickly. This is how I positively use the information about my family's medical history— I take precautions with myself and my children and have myself checked regularly.

You can use the knowledge you have from your family history and/ or genetic testing to work with your doctor and modify your behavior to try and prevent whatever it is from showing up in your life. You can be monitored regularly to ensure if you get cancer, you find it early. Early detection is very important to a patient's long-term prognosis. There are screenings and diagnostic tests that can be done to keep an eye on your health. Knowledge is power.

Just because you have a particular type of cancer in your family doesn't mean you're going to get cancer. And, if you do get it, your outcome isn't guaranteed to be the outcome of those who came before you. Science is constantly evolving, and one day, hopefully, cancer will be a thing of the past. What I know for sure is expecting to get cancer just because people in your family have been diagnosed with it isn't going to serve you well. In fact, it can impact you negatively. I'm a big believer in the saying, "What we think, we become." Don't think about getting cancer, nothing good can come of it. Do what you can to help yourself stay as healthy as possible, use the knowledge you gain from any genetic testing done by you or other members of your family, and stop obsessing about the unknown. Don't walk around expecting yourself to have a date with cancer one day in your future.

Going through breast cancer, sitting in the chemo room and meeting brave and courageous people who go to battle every day, I learned a lot. I never figured out why I got cancer at this time in my life, and I've given up trying. It's wasted energy. When I'm sitting at the cancer center, waiting for my check-up, I still look around the room and ask myself how I got here. But that's the thing, how do any of us get anywhere? How do kids and teachers become victims in a school shooting? How does a mother die during childbirth? There are no answers to these questions. It's easy to say bad things happen to good people, but the reality is, they do. That's just life.

I've struggled to make peace with the fact that I was diagnosed with cancer at age 42. I don't like having it as part of my history. I also know there isn't anything I can do about it. I can fight it all I want, but at the end of the day, it's always going to be part of me. Acceptance is a blessing. When I finally stopped trying to rewrite my story, I began to heal.

Sometimes my daughters hug me so tightly I can't breathe. They cling to me, and I know it's because of what our family went through. I know it's the residual effects of the fear they were forced to look directly in the eye. They were scared I would die.

When another mom gets diagnosed with breast cancer, the anxiety they experienced when I was diagnosed comes out again. The older they get, the easier it is for them to process the fear they have of cancer and the deeper our conversations have become. But it's still there. Over time, I'm sure it will continue to decrease, but some of it will always remain.

They will be monitored as they get older, and if breast cancer does knock at their door, there's no reason why they wouldn't catch it early. Again, knowledge is power. We'll use it to keep them both healthy.

TIP 24: WHEN A FAMILY MEMBER GETS SICK, THE WHOLE FAMILY IS IMPACTED

A cancer diagnosis doesn't just affect the person who is sick, the whole family is impacted. Since treatment for cancer is usually spread out over many weeks or months, your daily routine will probably change. Your family life will more than likely be disrupted, at least for several months. It will take a little time to get used to your "new normal." You might feel guilty about the burden your illness is placing on your family emotionally and even financially. If you have young children, you might feel badly about them having to be exposed to a part of life you didn't want them to face until they were older. I absolutely understand. However, you need to remember that you didn't ask to be diagnosed with cancer. It isn't your fault. Shit just happens.

TRIBE TIP

If you've had cancer and are now watching someone in your family go through the same type of cancer, you might feel guilty. You might blame yourself for passing on the genetic makeup that causes cancer. I've seen this happen many times. But it's not your fault. For example, if you've been through breast cancer and now your daughter has breast cancer, remember, you didn't do anything to cause this. You can't control your genetic makeup. Instead of feeling guilty about it, do everything you can to help your family member get through their diagnosis and treatment. Don't walk around blaming yourself. It's wasted energy.

Genetic testing is becoming more advanced and hopefully this will continue. If you've done genetic testing and you tested positive for a certain type of cancer, this can be helpful information to pass on to other members of your family. However, make sure you think about when you want to tell them. You don't want to give anyone information when they're too young to understand what it means. Talk to your genetic counselor to fully understand the results of your test and what this means for the members of your family.

Use the knowledge you learn to empower people, not scare them.

Nothing lasts forever.
We can spend our lives
worrying about
death, or we can decide
to live each day to the fullest.
**Your life,
your choice.**

CHAPTER 13

GETTING CANCER MAKES YOU THINK ABOUT YOUR DEATH

Here's the dark truth: getting a cancer diagnosis forces you to think about death. I promised you I would be completely honest in this book. I wouldn't be keeping my promise if I didn't address this. I don't care how early you find your cancer or what your prognosis is, hearing you have the "Big C" is probably going to cause you to think about your mortality. After all, you're human, and unfortunately, we don't live forever.

No one wants to think about dying. We all know it's going to happen someday, but we don't talk about it. We tuck it away, out of sight, and if we're lucky, we don't have to see it for a long time. It's easier and safer that way. But sometimes life has other plans for us. Sometimes life forces us to think about the absolute worst-case scenario and deal with it head on.

That's what happened to me. Being diagnosed with breast cancer—even though I found it early and had a positive prognosis—made me think about my greatest fear: passing away and leaving my two daughters alone in the world without me. I really struggled with this and it caused me a lot of sadness and anxiety for a long time. What helped me the most was when I stopped pushing the thought of my death away and actually let myself think about it. This might sound silly, but for a moment, let yourself think about what would happen if the worst-case scenario occurred. What would that even be?

One day, I let myself go there, to that dark place. I let my mind think about how it would be and what it would look like. I thought about how much I miss my mom and how I carry her with me, always. I thought about how when something happens that reminds me of her, I talk about her. This keeps her in my life. It wasn't always like this. At first, I couldn't even talk about her, just the mention of her name would bring me to tears. But over time, it got easier. There are still times I cry. I miss her with every part of my being, but I know she's with me. I have learned to live in a world without her because I didn't have a choice.

That's what I would want my daughters to do with me. I would want them to carry me with them and keep me in their thoughts. To hold on tight to the memories they have of me and remember all the wonderful experiences we had together. I would want them to know that death might separate us, but the love we have for each other can never die. Most importantly, I would want them to not let my death decrease the quality of their days, but to keep moving forward, living and enjoying life. I would never want them to become so consumed with sadness over my death that they couldn't enjoy and make the most of their lives.

When I took time to think about my death, I made peace with it. That doesn't mean I want to die anytime soon. It just means I allowed myself to go there, and what I realized is my daughters would be OK. It would be hard and they would struggle, but they would make it. They have people in their lives who love and care about them and who would make sure they pulled through. Knowing this comforted me.

Once you face your worst nightmare and realize things will be OK, you don't have to think about it anymore. You can give up all the worry and fear you have about it and concentrate on living, on getting healthy and making the most of each day of your life. Isn't that the goal? To make the most of each day of our beautiful lives?

TIP 25: FACE YOUR FEAR OF DEATH AND WRITE A LETTER TO YOUR LOVED ONES

I decided I wanted to write a letter to my kids. While I plan to dance at their weddings and hold my grandchildren, if life should deal me an unfair hand, as it has to other people, I wanted to make sure I said some things to my kids. While I had written little notes to my daughters and husband the night before my surgery, they were just a few scribbled sentences. This letter was intentionally written with a lot of time and thought put into it. Feel free to use or modify this letter, or make up your own. Write down whatever you want your family to know if something should happen to you. Put it in an envelope that hopefully won't need to be opened for a really long time. Don't rush through whatever it is you want to write to your family. Take the time to think about what you want to say, write it and then put it away. You'll feel good knowing if something should happen to you, your family will receive your words. And, if this isn't something you want to do, that's absolutely fine. No judging here. Ever. This is the letter I wrote.

To my children:

It's strange to think that one day I won't be here with you. When I sit and think about this it makes me sad. It's not something I do often, because who wants to think about death? I can think of lots of other ways to spend my time. However, I have things to say to you and I wanted to make sure you hear them. In case I'm not around to nag you, here's a list of important things I want you to always remember.

1. Miss me. Think of me. Remember me. But, don't let my death become the focus of your life. You have beautiful lives ahead of you. Make the most of your time. Don't get stuck in grief or focus too much of your energy on what you've lost or don't have. It's wasted energy and time.

2. Carry me with you, especially when you watch a sunset or see stars in the sky. I'll be smiling down on you, covering you with my love and wrapping you in a warm embrace.

3. We've had amazingly fun moments. Times when we laughed so hard we cried. Remember the good times and don't focus on the bad moments. When I yelled at you, it was because you deserved it and needed to hear what I had to say. One day, you'll be a parent and you'll understand.

4. Nothing is perfect in life: not you, not me, not our relationship. The same goes for your other relationships. If you're looking for perfection, you'll never be happy. Instead, look for the good in people. It's there.

5. The world is a beautiful place. Find the beauty that's all around you, even in your darkest moments. Even when you don't think you're strong enough to handle something. Remember, I know you are.

6. Don't take anything for granted. Ever.

7. Spend money on things that speak to your heart, but remember life is about the people you love, not the things you have. It's fun to have nice stuff, but it's even better to have people to share your life with.

8. Don't fight over my jewelry. Seriously.

9. If Daddy gets remarried, be nice to his new wife. I'll always be your Mom, but you have room in your life for a new friend.

10. If I'm in a hospital bed for a significant amount of time, please make sure you pluck the chin hairs from my face. It's not fun, but someone's got to do it.

11. The decision to marry someone is one of the biggest decisions of your life. Take it seriously and marry for love.

12. Find someone who will be willing to stay up with the baby, change diapers with you and laugh even when times are hard. Everyone has hard times.

13. Get a job you love so much you forget it's work. Something that feeds your soul and that you're passionate about.

14. Surround yourself with people who make you feel good about yourself and who love and accept you for who you are. Ditch the rest. You don't need negative people in your life.

15. Be honest, always, but deliver the truth with kindness.

16. If I don't get to meet your children tell them all about me. Especially the juicy parts.

17. Treat yourself with kindness and respect and demand this from other people.

18. Take care of your body and don't do anything you don't want to do. Ever. Remember, happy people are beautiful.

19. Cherish each other and be good to one another, always. There's nothing like a sibling.

20. Never forget how much you are loved. Always and forever.

Love,

Mom

The most important thing is to not let your fear of death get in the way of living your life.

TRIBE TIP

Don't be surprised if the patient wants to talk about his or her mortality. Hearing the words, "You have cancer," will absolutely make someone recognize how precious life is and how limited our time is. Even though this can be uncomfortable to discuss, take your cues from the patient. If they bring up certain things or even say, "In case something happens to me, I want you to know..." be there to listen. Dealing with cancer isn't easy. For anyone.

Hold on to faith.
Part of life
is navigating the roads,
not knowing if you're
going down the right one.
**Hoping you get
where you want to be
in the end.**
At some point,
you just have to let it go
and trust it will all work out.

SECTION 2

YOU SURVIVED.
NOW IT'S TIME TO THRIVE.

SECTION 2: INTRODUCTION

I wasn't the same person after cancer. Being diagnosed, going through treatment and seeing all that I saw along my journey had transformed me. Not only did I not recognize myself physically, what I wanted out of life had completely changed. The goals I had set before going through cancer seemed unimportant. I would look in the mirror and see a bald stranger staring back at me. Even more unfamiliar was who she was on the inside.

Everything felt off.

Disorienting.

Perplexing.

The world around me had remained the same and life had carried on while I was dealing with cancer. I was the one who was different, and the life I had lived before cancer wasn't what I wanted anymore. I recognized there wasn't anything wrong with my previous life, it just didn't fit anymore. The trivial things I used to worry about before I got sick were now insignificant. Meaningless problems, pointless emotional conflicts or fake friendships weren't what I wanted to spend my time on. I had been through challenging times and seen how hard life could be, for me and for others. I didn't take being on the other side of cancer for granted.

I valued my time.

I knew it was fleeting.

I didn't want to waste it.

I didn't want to be around negative people who brought me down or looked for ways to cause drama in my life. I wanted to seize life with both hands, to make the most of each day, every moment. There wasn't room for anyone who wanted to derail me or slow me down.

It took a little time for me to figure out what I wanted, but ultimately it was really quite simple:

- positive interactions with the people I love;

- to feel happy and content, calm and peaceful, joyful and blessed;

- to live hard and well and find meaning in each day;

- to make a positive contribution to the world and help other people.

But this didn't happen overnight.

I had to be patient and give myself time to learn how to make peace with my cancer diagnosis. It was hard not to let fear get in the way of living my life. I recognized I could let what I had been through enhance my life, or I could allow anxiety and "what if" thoughts to sabotage my future. I didn't want the fear to take over, but I also didn't want to forget about all I had been through. Finding that balance was a challenge. I knew my life would be fuller and richer if I could get to a place of deep appreciation and gratitude for what I had gone through instead of being upset it had happened to me and afraid it might happen again.

It took time, but eventually it happened...

I learned how to not just survive, but thrive.

My laugh became louder.

I felt free and light.

I became a joy seeker.

I worried less about what other people thought of me and instead filled my days with what I cared about. For the first time, I lived life on my own terms. Since I had been given a second chance at life, I didn't want to waste one single moment. I started making decisions with intention instead of just allowing life to happen, and I didn't base my life on other people's definitions of success.

When you go through a traumatic situation of any kind, you will come out on the other side a changed person. How could you not? We learn from our challenges and gain a new perspective—if we let ourselves.

The hard part is determining how the "new you" fits into your old life. Give yourself time to figure this out and don't be afraid to embrace the new you. There are lots of positive takeaways after you survive a difficult experience. Use what you've learned to create and live your best life.

Don't hold back.

Don't let fear get in the way.

Grasp your life with both hands and insist on living the life you want.

I'll show you how in this section of the book. You can absolutely learn to thrive after you survive. While it won't be easy, you can make peace with your diagnosis, shut down the fear and live a very meaningful life.

Whatever you think,
you're right.
Believe you can and you will.
Believe you can't and you won't.
Your life, your choice.

CHAPTER 14

CONSIDER YOURSELF A SURVIVOR

After my surgeries and treatments were over, I was a mess. I was constantly experiencing all types of feelings.

Feelings I never knew existed.

Feelings I didn't want to deal with but couldn't suppress.

One minute I was thankful and appreciative of my life and the next minute I was unhappy, feeling sorry for myself or pissed off at the universe. I could experience any or all of these emotions throughout my day and I never knew when something would trigger a negative response. Sometimes I didn't even need a reason to feel down in the dumps. Other times I would start the day off calm and confident, then someone would say something to me and my insecurities would kick in. I was shocked at how easily I could move from being OK to feeling anxious and worried about my future.

It was uncomfortable, to say the least. I didn't know how to find peace, get my confidence back and move forward.

I wanted to have faith everything would be fine.

I wanted to be promised cancer was out of my life forever.

I wanted to feel safe and secure.

As you're adjusting to life as a survivor, you might feel like you're on an emotional rollercoaster. You might feel frustrated and want to yell and scream at someone. Be aware of your potentially short fuse and try not to take your frustration out on the people you love. Instead, go into a room, shut the door and scream as loudly as you can. Hit your pillow. Punch a punching bag. Tell cancer to fuck off, that you're going to win, that it messed with the wrong person.

I remember being alone in my basement, staring in a mirror and deciding I wanted to scream. It wasn't planned, it was just something that came to me. At first, I screamed like a wimp. I could hardly even hear what I was saying. "Louder," I thought, "I need to scream louder." So I did. By the end of my session, I was screaming so loudly I wouldn't be surprised if the neighbors could hear. I didn't care. It felt great. I was getting my anger out. I was doing something positive to help myself deal with my frustration.

After that episode, whenever I started feeling overwhelmed or pissed off, I would wait until my family was out of the house, then curse like a sailor. It felt so good, and no one knew I did it.

A very important part of surviving after being diagnosed is learning how to live knowing you once had cancer in your body. You're happy to be done with treatments and you want to move on with your after-cancer life, but you might feel like there's a black cloud hanging over your head. You might not trust you're OK. You can't pretend shit doesn't happen anymore because you've witnessed firsthand it does. Not just to other people, but to you and your family. And since it's happened before, why wouldn't it happen again?

You might find you're living life from one doctor's appointment to the next. I used to do this too. When I left my doctor's office, I would think, "I'm good for three months. I don't have to worry right now because my doctor said things looked good." I would do everything I could to live my life as normally as possible until the next appointment or blood check. A few days before, I would find myself worrying. What would she discover? Would something pop up in the results and my life be completely thrown off-kilter like it was when I was originally diagnosed?

Do you find yourself doing this? It's not uncommon for cancer survivors to divide their lives into increments of time between one doctor's visit and the next. Eventually, you will start to feel more comfortable. You will start to trust things will be OK. That you'll be OK. After a while, your doctor will tell you it's time to space out your appointments. You might have six months or even a year in between checkups, which is a good sign.

You don't want to rush through your life or wish it away, but at the same time you understand the longer cancer stays away, the safer you are. You want to hit the two-, five-, and ten-year marks of being in remission while making the most of each day. How do you do this? How do you move on after a cancer diagnosis, take the lessons you've learned, make the most of each day and not let the fear of a reoccurrence get in the way of enjoying your life?

This is the million-dollar question, right? Don't worry, we're going to get there.

Unfortunately, your innocence is lost once you go through cancer. If you haven't figured it out by now, your life will never be the same. Ever. You will probably always have an oncologist, and there will be doctor's appointments and various ways to monitor things to make sure you stay healthy. There will more than likely always be a little part of you—regardless of how many years you've been in remission, how early you found your cancer or how aggressive your treatment was—that fears it will happen again. This is normal. The more you distance yourself between the date of your diagnosis and the present moment, the more confident you will feel. But your life is still forever changed.

You understand how fragile life is.

You understand that bad things can happen to good people.

You understand there are no guarantees. For anyone.

You have two choices. Door number one opens to a dark path. You will be fearful all the time and it will make you negative and not a whole lot of fun to be around. You will constantly worry about your health or the health of a loved one. Instead of living your life, you will give into the fear and let it take over. You will think about cancer and wonder if it's lurking in your body. You will obsess about why you or your loved one got cancer in the first place.

Thank goodness for door number two. Behind this door is gratitude and joy. You stop taking things for granted and appreciation becomes your middle name. You feel fortunate for every day you're alive. You wake up knowing how blessed you are. You try to make the most of the time you have with your loved ones and not let the fear of cancer or anything else get in the way. You actively decide to live hard and well and have faith that everything will be OK. You choose not to obsess about what might or might not happen. You don't have time to worry, you're too busy living.

I highly recommend door number two. However, even when you choose this option, there will be times when fear seeps into your day. What do you do? How do you handle it?

You start by taking one day at a time. One minute at a time. You do the best you can with the hand you've been dealt. You look for the positive, even when it seems nearly impossible to find. Even when you think you aren't strong enough to deal with whatever you have going on, you dig deep inside yourself and remember you are strong. You are brave. You can handle whatever life tosses your way. You have to believe in yourself and hold on to hope. At the same time, give yourself a break if you're still afraid—you've been through a lot.

At lunch with a friend, I admitted to being scared about having a reoccurrence. I felt fear every time I had a pain in my body or even got a cold. I didn't want to be a hypochondriac or automatically think, "Oh no, is it cancer?" But it was difficult.

I'll never forget what my friend told me: "You have to tell yourself all the time you're going to be fine, and one day you will truly believe it."

This was by far the absolute best advice anyone gave me. Are you paying attention? This will help you.

TIP 26: DECIDE YOU'RE A SURVIVOR

You must learn to think of yourself as a cancer survivor. Yes, a survivor. It doesn't matter what you were diagnosed with or what the statistics are, you've got to play to win. You must believe you're going to be OK. You aren't going to move forward if you don't think you can. You have to think of yourself as being a person who was diagnosed with cancer, went through the treatment plan—whatever it was—and now it's time to move on. Even if you're dealing with a chronic or advanced cancer situation, think of yourself as a survivor. Say these words:

"I'm a survivor."

"I'm going to be OK."

"I can crush cancer."

I know it sounds too simple, but it really does work. Tell yourself you're going to be OK, even if you aren't totally convinced. It doesn't matter what anyone else thinks. What does matter is that you believe, and the best way to start believing you're going to be OK is to start saying it to yourself. This isn't a pipe dream or an empty exercise. What you tell yourself can have a profound impact on your life. You've got to transition from being a patient to living as a survivor. You must believe with all your heart that you dealt with your illness and you're moving on. Enjoy one day at a time and expect to live a really long life.

TIP 27: MAKE SURE YOU'RE COMFORTABLE WITH HOW YOU'RE BEING MONITORED

You need doctors who are on top of their game, up-to-date on the latest research and medical advancements, and who are committed to helping you crush cancer. You also need to go to a doctor who is caring. A person who sees you as an individual, not a statistic or just another person with cancer. My doctors each have the patience of a saint. I can't tell you how many times I've asked, "Am I going to be OK?" or "Do you think things are going well?" or "I've read about X or Y, should we do this?" (Since I have a laptop and the ability to google, that makes me an expert, right?) They listen to and answer my questions with kindness and understanding. They never judge me when I call the office spouting off my latest concern. They understand how disquieting living life as a cancer survivor can be, and they're always there for me.

Talk to your doctor about how you will be monitored going forward and how often you will be seen. This will depend on the type of cancer you were diagnosed with and at what stage it was found. Some people feel more comfortable seeing their doctor every few months, other people only want to go once a year. Discuss this with your doctor and establish a surveillance plan you both feel comfortable with. Be diligent with your health, and if you notice any changes, call your doctor's office and schedule an appointment. Feeling good about your follow-up procedure will help you manage your fear of having a reoccurrence.

TRIBE TIP

Be there to listen when the survivor opens up and wants to talk. Don't judge, just listen. Remember, he or she is working through a lot of internal issues and might need encouragement from you. Be there to give it.

I am strong.
I am healthy.
**I have faith I am
on the right path.**
I trust the universe.
I am blessed.

CHAPTER 15

YOU NEED A MANTRA

My doctors did a great job focusing on the physical aspects of my cancer diagnosis. I wouldn't be here if I didn't have a brilliant medical team who treated me with all the wonderful tools available. They ran tests, prescribed medications, did surgery to cut out the problem area, used radiation and fed my body drugs to kill any cancer cells that might be lurking.

But the cancer wasn't just impacting my body, my mind was directly affected as well. In fact, dealing with the effects cancer had on my mind was just as challenging as the physical issues. The doctors could see the physical problem and fix it. The scary thoughts I kept having, the scenarios I would play over and over again in my head, these didn't show up on a scan or blood test. I was the only one who heard them over and over again, and I had to decide on my own I wanted to help myself mentally.

I felt like my body had failed me and I was terrified and furious. I made such an effort to take care of myself and did all the "right" things. How did my body thank me? By getting cancer. "Thanks a lot," I would tell my body, "Good to know I can count on you." There had been something quietly lurking inside me while I was busy living life, and I had no idea. This is especially chilling about cancer.

It's sneaky.

You don't know it's there.

It takes over silently.

You might feel you were duped by your own body. How could you have cancer and not know about it? It waits quietly and attacks when its victim is unsuspecting. You're unprepared for its unwelcome visit, so you don't know what to do when it happens. It makes you recognize how vulnerable you are.

I was mad at my body, but I was also embarrassed about getting cancer. I'm not sure why, and in retrospect, I realize this was silly. I knew there wasn't anything I did to cause the cancer, but in some ways I felt like it was my fault. It was my body, and if I'm in charge of my body, it must be my fault, right? I would go in and out of mentally being in a good place. Some days I would think about all the treatments I did and feel confident I would be OK. Other days fear would be my greatest enemy, staring me down when I wanted to feel safe. I was driving myself crazy. This was such a hard way to live and I knew I needed to do something about it. My body and mind needed to be on the same team. It wasn't serving me well to judge myself.

What helped me the most, and what I promise will help you, is to establish a mantra.

You might be thinking, "What is a mantra and how is it going to help me?"

A mantra is a phrase or word you say to yourself repeatedly. Something that resonates with you and is easy to remember, that you can repeat over and over again when you find yourself feeling scared, worried or having negative thoughts. It can be anything. If you don't think this will work or you think it's silly, think again.

It works.

It will help you.

Do it.

You can come up with your own mantra or use something that speaks to your heart. Maybe you've seen something on social media or in a book you find empowering. Perhaps there's a Bible passage that brings you peace, a music lyric or a line from a poem. It doesn't matter, as long as it speaks to you, inspires you or comforts you.

I wanted to come up with something that would help me feel better every time the scary thoughts started entering my head, which seemed to be all the time. I needed something to stop these thoughts from taking over. I wanted to be armed and ready to shut them down before they could get me all worked up. My mantra was my weapon. It was my saving grace.

The following 12 words became my first mantra:

I am strong.

I am healthy.

I am cured.

I am blessed.

Here's why it worked for me: Instead of telling myself I was weak for getting cancer, I told myself I was strong and could deal with it. Instead of telling myself I was sick, I reminded myself I was healthy. Instead of worrying about the cancer coming back, I told myself I was cured. Instead of feeling sorry for myself and my situation, I focused on my many blessings.

Each morning, when I wrote in my journal, I would write down my mantra. The more I wrote it and said it to myself, the more I started to believe it. I printed it and kept it in a picture frame by my bathroom sink. Every morning it was there to greet me, reminding me exactly what I needed to believe. I brushed my teeth to these words, washed my face to them, and looked at them while I put on my makeup. You'd be surprised how much time we spend at our bathroom sink. This is actually a great place to put encouraging notes and messages to yourself. I have a bulletin board there now. When I find something I like—a picture, quote or card—I hang it on my bulletin board and look at it every time I go into my bathroom.

At first I didn't naturally remember to say these four sentences, I had to actively remind myself. It was easier to let my mind return to its familiar, scary thoughts. It took work to recognize when my brain was going to the dark side and intentionally replace my negativity with inspirational words.

But after a little time and practice, I noticed my mind started automatically going to the four sentences. I would take a deep breath in between each sentence, which would help relax me. I could say them to myself at any time throughout my day and I would immediately feel better. I could sit in the waiting room at the hospital, nervous for an appointment, and say my mantra to myself. I could be at a party and hear someone say something that would have set me off before, but now I had my comforting words to turn to. If I couldn't fall asleep, I could lie in bed and say it over and over again in my head until I dozed off. The best part was no one had any idea what I was thinking. They didn't have to because it was just for me. The more I said it to myself, the faster my body and mind relaxed. It was pure power. It was my secret weapon and I could carry it with me all the time.

TIP 28: YOUR MANTRA

It's time to create or find your personal mantra. It doesn't matter who you are, what you've gone through or what you're currently facing, everyone needs a mantra. Don't just do this quickly or haphazardly, put some time into it. Think about what words or phrases will help and empower you. Look at the words to your favorite songs, Bible passages or poems. Look on social media for quotes that inspire you. Everyone has words that speak to their heart. What works for me might not work for you. You're more than welcome to use my mantra, but only if it truly resonates with you.

Come up with a phrase that gives you strength and comfort, especially when you start to feel nervous or fear is staring you in the face and won't leave you alone. Find the words that make you feel the way you want, whether it be peaceful, strong, joyful, or cured.

My first mantra was four sentences long, but the length doesn't really matter. It just shouldn't be too lengthy or overly complicated—you don't want to struggle to remember it when you need it.

I design a new mantra for myself each year, based on what is going on in my life. Different words speak to me at different times. I like to create them at the beginning of the year, but you can change yours at any time or keep it as long as you wish.

Commit to reciting your mantra on a regular basis. This is especially important when you first start using it. It seems so simple, and it is, but the benefits are huge.

TRIBE TIP

Pay attention to your loved one's mental state. If you notice a change in their behavior or if they seem sad or depressed, you might encourage them to seek the guidance of a counselor, priest or rabbi. I briefly touched on this in Section 1 when I recommended the patient consider talking with a counselor. They might not have done it during treatment and need to talk with someone now. If you feel they would benefit from talking with a professional or joining a support group for people who have been through cancer, consider mentioning it. Tell the survivor you're just trying to help, that you aren't judging them. It is not a sign of weakness to get help when we find ourselves struggling with a difficult situation. In fact, it's a sign of strength. I've seen many people deal with the physical issues associated with a cancer diagnosis but not address the mental challenges. A lot of hospitals offer this service to cancer patients and survivors, and they have support groups already established. You can call the cancer center to learn about the specific programs offered in your area.

Have faith that things
will work out.
Hope for the best.
Believe good things
are coming your way.
Trust that your dreams
will come true.

CHAPTER 16

FAITH VERSUS FEAR

There are many things in our lives we can't control, and this can cause a great deal of anxiety and fear. It's scary to think about all the bad things that can happen to us or the people we love. Everyone has something they worry about, and if you or someone you love has been through cancer, you get to carry around an extra fear, the fear you might get cancer, or if you've already been through it, the fear of it coming back. I will never dismiss this very real fear. It's there, and it sucks.

But if we give into this fear, we end up wasting a lot of time worrying about what might or might not happen. This doesn't help and it also won't change anything. In fact, I would argue that spending time thinking and worrying about cancer can actually hurt you. So how do you live with the fear of cancer and not let it mess up your life?

It's normal to worry about cancer, especially right after you finish your treatments. You have to decide you aren't going to let your mind go there. And when it inevitably does, you have to actively force yourself to dismiss your negative thoughts and replace them with positive ones.

After I finished all my treatments I was still terrified of cancer. I would calculate how old I was and the approximate years my daughters would graduate from college, get married or have kids. I would think to myself, "If I can live for five years, I'll get to see them do X," or, "If I can make it fifteen years, they'll be this age and probably be doing Y."

This wasn't any way to live, and I was actually getting on my own nerves. I realized I wasn't helping myself by worrying about the future, I was ruining my present by filling my mind with thoughts of cancer instead. I decided I could go through life worrying about what might or might not happen to me or my family, or I could choose to have faith.

You can spend your time giving into your anxiety, or you can decide to move forward. Have you ever wanted to do something, but when you thought about it you felt shivers of fear race through your body? You were convinced something would go wrong? Instead of holding onto faith, you went to the other side. You let the fear of what might happen keep you from doing what you really wanted to do. Most of us have experienced moments when we were consumed by the fear caused by "what if" thinking, the fear that things will go wrong. It's easy to go down this path and, once you start, often hard to stop. We get caught up in our negative thinking and don't realize the scary words we say to ourselves are contributing to our fear.

Then there's faith, the ability to believe deep in your soul that things will turn out OK. You might currently feel like your faith has seriously been tested. A cancer diagnosis can do that. There will be times when life gives you a dose of something you don't want. However, most of the time things work out fine and there's no sense in worrying about what could or might happen. We really have no control over our lives. I know this is an unsettling thought, but it's true. What we can control is how we deal with the challenges we face.

I was raised in a family that was moderately religious. We observed holidays, prayed weekly together, and growing up, God was part of my life. My faith was something I had been taught to cherish. However, when my mom passed away, I really struggled with my faith. I had trouble understanding why something bad had happened to someone so good, and I carried this around with me. I became angry at God and never really made peace with it. I had read plenty of books and talked to many religious scholars, but I still struggled. How could I make sense of something that was so nonsensical to me? As a result, when I was diagnosed with cancer, God wasn't the first place I turned. I've met many people who have an extremely strong faith and believe, "It's in God's hands." I've seen people sit in the chemo room and read the Bible, holding on to their faith and keeping it close. I've been jealous of these people because of the comfort they get from having such a strong belief. For many people, going through a serious illness strengthens their relationship with God.

I'm still trying to figure it all out, but here's what I know for sure: We have to intentionally decide to have faith. Faith that everything will turn out the way we want it to, because most of the time it does. Faith that our kids will be safe, our plane will land, everyone we love will remain healthy, including ourselves, and that everything will be OK. You can actively decide to give up your fear and trust your medical team, the universe, God, yourself. You do what you can, control what you can and let go of the rest. Carrying around a bag of fear isn't going to serve you well.

I've spent many sleepless nights tossing and turning because fear was right there in bed with me. (I've warned you about googling scary cancer stories at night when you want to go to sleep. This is a surefire way to invite fear into your bedroom.) What did I do in these situations? First, I learned to recognize what would probably set me off. For me, when I hear about a person who went through treatment for breast cancer and had a reoccurrence, it makes me anxious, especially if it's a mom with young children. Since I know this about myself now, I'm able to actively decide to replace my thoughts of anxiety with thoughts that help me feel better. I think about all I did to give myself the best possible prognosis and I remember how blessed I truly am. I remind myself every person is different, every cancer is different, every scenario is different. Instead of dwelling on the scary thoughts, I focus on my mantra, I write in my journal, I do deep breathing exercises. This usually does the trick. If it doesn't, I go exercise. I take a long walk, practice yoga or even lift some weights.

I was diagnosed in April so I tend to feel more anxious in the spring. Subconsciously I think about what I went through when I was diagnosed and what my family had to deal with. I've learned to pay attention to my feelings, and now I give myself an extra dose of self-care each year around this time. I schedule fun and relaxing activities for myself and talk to my friends and family about what I went through. My daughters also tend to get anxious each year around this time. I try to pay more attention to them as well and give them lots of love and encouragement. When we try to ignore how we're feeling and push the fear away, it tends to want to stick around even more. When we recognize it for what it is, we can deal with it and move forward.

One way I've learned to decrease my fear of cancer is by doing everything I can to be healthy. Instead of spending time worrying, I spend time taking care of myself. I eat well and exercise, surround myself with positive people, go to the doctor, get the sleep I need and take my recommended medication and vitamins. I make sure I manage my stress and help myself stay mentally strong by practicing yoga and meditation, writing in my journal and saying my mantra. I purposely schedule a little downtime every day, take a hot bath every evening and don't take life too seriously. I laugh often and try to have fun. All of these activities help me decrease my fear because I'm taking positive action. Don't underestimate the power of taking care of yourself.

If a negative thought crosses my mind, I don't give it power—after all, it's just a thought. I let it pass, then focus on all the good things. You can learn to do this too. You can spend your day worrying about what might go wrong, what could happen and all the things you can't control, but it isn't going to do anything but hurt you. You'll be focusing on negativity, sabotaging your present moments and stealing your joy. Instead, decide to have faith that all will be good, that the universe is on your side, that the bad things you know can happen, won't. And, if something does happen, have faith that you will be able to get through it. Remind yourself you've done it before and you can do it again.

The key is to understand you're going to have moments of anxiety. You can learn to deal with them and to be resilient. What do resilient people have in them that keeps them going, even when it seems impossible? What is it about some people who have faced seriously difficult situations but have the ability to keep on keeping on? People who are resilient believe good things are coming. Instead of giving up, they fight. They're optimistic about their future. When they start to question their resolve, they push themselves onward. They love and cherish life, even when it gets hard. They cheer themselves on instead of holding themselves back and focus on what they have instead of what they have lost. They believe they can get through whatever they're facing; quitting is not an option for them. Their only option is moving forward, doing the best they can, taking one day at a time. Resilient people know that when life hands them a difficult situation, they have the strength inside themselves to get through it. This allows them to live with faith instead of fear.

The longer it's been since your diagnosis, the more relaxed you'll feel and the more confident you'll be in your ability to crush cancer. Always be patient with yourself and don't judge yourself for having heightened anxiety sometimes. You're doing the best you can, and it's enough. Spend your time living, not worrying.

TIP 29: MANAGE THE ANXIETY CAUSED BY SEEING YOUR DOCTOR

As a cancer survivor, there are definitely times when you feel more fearful than others. Many people, while they want to be monitored regularly, still stress about what their doctor might find at the appointment. Getting any type of scan, test or blood work done can also be a trigger. It's stressful waiting for results of any kind.

Don't be afraid to ask your doctor to call you with the results. You can even schedule a follow-up appointment with your doctor when you schedule the test so you'll know when to expect your results and have the time to discuss them. This takes a little of the unknown out of the equation. I get my blood work done the week before I meet with my doctor instead of having it taken on the same day. That way we have the results in front of us during my appointment and I can ask any questions I might have. If an appointment can't be scheduled, I ask to be called as soon as the results are available.

Another good way to reduce stress? Try not to schedule any kind of test at the end of the week. That way you're more likely to get your results before the weekend. It's no fun spending Friday night, Saturday and Sunday worrying about them.

TRIBE TIP

Try not to judge the survivor as he or she works through fear and searches for faith. Everyone has an individual relationship with God, and if you're someone who has a very strong faith, try not to be too hard on your friend or family member if you see them questioning theirs. This is normal. It's hard to understand why a person gets cancer and it's natural to be angry about it. It just takes time to sort through all of this and get to the other side. Be supportive, offer to lend an ear or provide any insight you can regarding your faith.

Feeling guilty about getting cancer is a wasted emotion.
It's not your fault and you didn't ask for it.
Instead, focus on what you can do to help yourself.

CHAPTER 17

STOP FEELING GUILTY ABOUT YOUR CANCER

A cancer patient often carries around a lot of guilt. In fact, one doesn't have to work very hard to find a reason to feel remorseful. Trust me, I'm speaking from experience. The guilt I felt ran deep and weighed me down. I don't want that to happen to you.

For starters, I felt guilty about getting cancer in the first place. Like I had a choice, right? Maybe there were things I could have done differently to prevent myself from getting cancer. Maybe this. Maybe that. I could spend hours going down the maybe path. Truthfully, I thought I could have been more in tune with my body and gone to the doctor sooner. I remember discovering a lump, but I didn't have it checked immediately. I tried to convince myself it was nothing because I didn't want to be a hypochondriac. After my diagnosis, I felt horrible about this delay and kept telling myself I should have taken care of it sooner. Maybe I could have prevented the whole thing from happening, or at least I wouldn't have had to go through chemo. Eventually I learned to put this thought behind me and focus on the fact that I did go to the doctor and followed the recommended treatment. Instead of feeling badly about getting cancer in the first place, I became grateful I took care of it when I did. There's no point in driving yourself crazy trying to pin down what you did wrong to get cancer or what you could have done better to prevent it. It's wasted energy.

Another cause of my guilt was the strain it put on my friends and family. The people who loved me were stressed about my diagnosis. Plus, when I wasn't feeling well, being around me wasn't much fun. A lot of people did a ton of nice things for me and inconvenienced themselves. I felt badly about this. I didn't want to be a source of worry for people who cared about me and I didn't like asking for help, much less needing help. Here's what I realized. When you love someone, you take the good and the bad. If someone I cared about was diagnosed with cancer, I would happily help them and wouldn't think twice about it.

Dealing with cancer can also be expensive. I had a lot of doctor's appointments, procedures and surgeries, not to mention the prescription drugs I was taking (Don't skimp on the nausea medicine!). The medical bills added up to a hefty sum of money. We could afford it, but I felt guilty about having to spend money on it. Even if you have good insurance, going through cancer is still going to cost you. I'm sure you can think of a lot of other ways you would rather spend your money, but you don't really have a choice. Chalk it up to "it is what it is" and move on.

Then there was the survivor's guilt. I had met wonderful people who had been diagnosed with cancer and they didn't make it. Some of them were even younger than I was. I felt sorry for them and their friends and family. Why did they pass away and I didn't? I also thought about my mom many times while I was on my journey, comparing my diagnosis to hers and feeling guilty about what she had gone through and that she never got better. I eventually learned to cut myself some slack when it came to this and recognize one situation didn't have anything to do with the other. I decided the best way to honor the people who passed away from cancer was to make the most of my life and be the best version of myself.

My greatest source of guilt came when I thought about what my illness had done to my kids. I struggled with this for a long time. Being diagnosed with the "Big C" when you have young children is more than hard—it's nearly impossible to endure. I wondered if I would live to see my kids grow up and thought about the permanent damage I had caused them. I often saw the fear they carried around and I felt sorry for them. They were forced to see their mom go through cancer and deal with the realization that life is uncertain. They found out bad things can happen to their family, and they really struggled with it.

The guilt was practically unbearable until I read a beautiful essay written by my daughter, Zoe, when she was 16. I'm sharing it with you because my kids aren't any different from yours. Remember, kids are strong, and there are positive lessons to be learned, even in our darkest hours. While I would never have wanted my kids to have to face my mortality at the ages they were when I was diagnosed, me feeling guilty wasn't useful to them or me. I had to learn to trust my kids would be OK and provide them with help when I thought they needed it. They are more compassionate now when it comes to other people and they understand how precious life is.

I didn't change anything in this essay or help her while she was writing it. These are completely her words and thoughts.

WHAT I LEARNED WHEN MY MOM GOT CANCER

One of the most horrifying, yet profound concepts of life is the naivety that as a child, you are shielded from all of the terrible things in life. When I was young, I thought that only bad things happened to bad people and that nothing terrible would ever happen to my family. I felt protected from all of the horrible things happening in the world. I knew that a war was going on in the Middle East and I knew that there were people going hungry every day. However, being the simple-minded fourteen-year-old girl that I was, I was unaware that everything I had initially believed about the world was wrong.

My perspective on life completely shifted in April of 2014 when I found out my mom had been diagnosed with breast cancer. I remember the day my world changed. My dad had picked me up after school, which was unusual because my mom was always the one who drove my sister and I home. When I got home that afternoon, something felt off; however, I proceeded with my usual after-school routine. I remember my dad asking me to come downstairs because we were going to have a family meeting. When I first got downstairs, I jokingly asked who got diagnosed with cancer. As those words came out of my mouth, my mom burst into tears. We all sat down on the couch after a few seconds of confusion between my sister and me. My dad reassured us that my mom had the "good" type of cancer. For me, cancer was just a sickness that caused death. I do not think that at the time I knew of anybody who had survived this horrible word.

My sister and I took the news very differently. For my sister, she let her emotions unfold rapidly and began to hyperventilate in front of my family. However, I kept my feelings somewhat reserved, then went upstairs to sob uncontrollably, feeling as if the walls were closing in on me. From the second I heard the news, a spirit of hope about the world changed inside of me. I felt like my childhood had been jolted from me against my will, and that cancer had pushed me towards adulthood and a sense of maturity I had never seen in myself before.

For three months, my sister and I slept in the same bed every night. Having each other as a security blanket may have been the only thing that kept me hopeful throughout the entire process. The day I walked in on my mom shaving her head was the hardest day of my life. Coming into her bedroom without knocking, looking at her once thick, beautiful dark brown hair lying on the bathroom floor was a moment that I will never forget. Throughout the next year, watching my mom suffer through her eight intense rounds of chemo, two surgeries, radiation, and trip to the hospital due to the violent vomiting and dehydration caused by the chemo, I knew that my mom was the strongest woman I had ever met.

I am lucky to say that my mom is a survivor, and although my introduction to adulthood was abrupt, I appreciate life more than I ever thought I could. My mom's diagnosis felt like the punishment for a crime that my family was wrongly convicted of. When I initially found out my mom had cancer, I saw no positives and at that moment I was not supposed to. I will never understand why bad things happen to good people, but I do understand that even though there are times in my life that I can't control, there are lessons that come out of every situation. After this experience, I don't take things for granted, I don't worry about the small stuff and I appreciate the people in my life.

While I am not glad that my family was forced to go through this ordeal, we are stronger and closer because of it, and for that I am forever thankful.

TIP 30: DON'T BE AFRAID TO HAVE THOSE HARD CONVERSATIONS

It sucks for you and for your loved ones to have to deal with the "Big C," but feeling badly about it isn't going to help you or them. If you're worried about them, let them know. If you're carrying a lot of guilt, sit everyone down and tell them how you feel. Get it off your chest so you can make peace with it and move on. Know what they'll say? I'd be willing to bet they will tell you they love you unconditionally, and while they wish you didn't have to go through it, they're happy to be there for you. And I bet you'd say the same thing to them if your roles were reversed. Instead of feeling guilty, use this time to grow your relationships, to tell people how special they are to you and what they mean to you. Get out of your comfort zone, open up and have those talks that might initially bring tears, but can result in strengthened relationships.

Trust that your kids will be OK. It's hard to watch them struggle with their feelings about your illness, but remember, it's not your fault. Get your kids professional help if you think they need to talk to a counselor and encourage them to open up about what they're feeling. Your kids will be taking their cues from you. If they see you moping around and having a pity party, they'll think that's how they should act. If they see you being positive and focusing on what you can do to help yourself, they will likely do the same. Our kids are watching all the time. Gulp.

TRIBE TIP

Whatever you do, don't make a survivor feel guilty for getting cancer. Don't weigh them down by telling them how worried you are, how expensive their treatment is or how hard it is on their friends and family. Definitely don't blame them for getting cancer or tell them it's their fault. Instead, shower them with love and be there to offer support. Build them up instead of tearing them down. Trust me, they already have plenty of guilt.

The scars on
my body are
my battle scars.
They remind me of what
I've been through and
what I've survived.
I am a warrior.

CHAPTER 18

CANCER ISN'T SEXY

One of the biggest changes cancer may bring, depending on the type you have and your treatment plan, may be the physical changes your body experiences.

Before cancer, I liked the way I looked. While I wasn't a runway model or even close, I was happy with my appearance and it was a positive part of my identity. I recognized the person in the mirror and I liked her. After cancer, I didn't recognize myself anymore. It was an unusual feeling, and one I didn't like.

It took a little time for me to get comfortable with the unwelcome changes that occurred. Our appearance and how we feel about it can impact our self-esteem. I suddenly felt insecure about how I looked, which made me even angrier about getting cancer. I never requested cancer, and I certainly didn't ask for the change in my appearance or the hit my self-confidence took.

My body went through a lot during my treatment. You might have noticed changes in your body as well. Before cancer, the only scar I had on my body was on my knee from falling when I was a child. I was running too fast and tripped over a rock in our back yard. It reminds me of my childhood and has never bothered me. Now I have many scars. I have scars from the port they used to give me chemo. I have scars from the double mastectomy I had and scars from the reconstruction. There are also the scars from the laparoscopic hysterectomy.

Scars aren't the only thing that changed my appearance. Since I did radiation, the treated breast is slightly different than the other one. I also opted to have my nipples removed during my double mastectomy. Because of this, I have three-dimensional nipple tattoos instead of normal nipples (I promised you the honest truth, so I'm giving it to you.). Other changes many cancer patients go through are changes in weight, muscle mass and hair. You also may have lasting physical side effects depending on the type of chemo and/or radiation you were given, if you had lymph nodes removed and the kind of surgery you had. These are just some of the joys of going through cancer.

It is my hope that you learn to accept how your body has changed. This doesn't mean you have to like the changes, but instead of judging yourself, try to thank your body for enduring and surviving. You've been through a lot, so of course your physical appearance shows it. It took me a little time to get used to my new body. I would see my scars and I didn't like them, especially when I got out of the shower and I was drying off—I would look into the mirror and see all the scars at one time. They were fully exposed and it made me sad. Eventually I learned to embrace my scars and feel proud of them. To look at them as my battle scars earned when life put me in a difficult situation and I rose to the challenge. But this took a long time and required lots of grace. As you begin to think of yourself as a survivor, embrace your scars and all the changes your body went through. In time, your hair will grow back, you will gain or lose weight depending on what you need to do and your scars will even fade.

This brings me to the super fun topic of sex. Yep, that three-letter word you might have wondered about but didn't want to bring up to your doctor. How embarrassing, right? You've got enough to think about, who wants to deal with sex? Well, you or your partner might, and we're going to go there. (If my kids or parents are reading this, you might want to skip to the next chapter. That would probably be best for all of us.)

When you go through cancer, you feel a lot of things, but I can't say sexy is one of them. It's hard to feel sexy when you're recovering from surgery, popping pills, exhausted or dealing with the effects of whatever treatment you've received. Constipation from the drugs I was taking immediately comes to mind. And nothing says "Come to bed" like a little vomit. I'm not going to lie to you, your sex life is going to take a temporary hit. Probably a big one. If you're one of those people who sails through your treatments and you feel like having sex, go for it. Bask in it. Embrace it. However, if you're someone who can't imagine having sex because you're just trying to get through the day, don't feel bad. It's all part of the cancer experience.

I can't say I was often in the mood to have sex. I had a lot of other things on my mind, like surviving. So I don't think our bedroom was a sexual wonderland while I was going through my treatment. When I was working on this chapter, I decided to ask my husband about it.

"When I was going through cancer, we didn't really have sex very often, did we?"

I asked this question out of the blue, but he's kind of used to me randomly asking him odd things.

"It's hard to remember, but I don't think so," he said.

"Did you mind? I mean, did you feel slighted?"

He looked at me with a serious expression on his face and said, "Did I feel slighted? No, I didn't feel slighted. I worried about a lot of things, but sex wasn't one of them."

I smiled at him because he's one of the good guys.

"Of course, if you want," he continued, "we can work really hard to make up for it. I'd be willing to do that for you."

Remember that open communication is your friend. Talk to your partner about what you're feeling. You don't want your diagnosis to come between you. While your sex life might be taking a hiatus, you can use this experience as an opportunity to grow together emotionally and even become closer to one another. Allow yourself to feel vulnerable and be honest about what you're thinking. You might not feel like having sex, but you can definitely talk.

If you aren't currently in a relationship, you might wonder if you will ever be able to meet anyone after going through cancer. You might think, "No one is going to want to be with me, I have scars on my body." Or "I'm broken, who would want to be with me?" Be patient with yourself. Give yourself time to get used to your body.

Eventually you will meet someone who makes you feel secure and comfortable and who admires you for your strength and courage.

What you truly need to work on is establishing a positive body image. Try to watch how you talk to yourself.

Don't view yourself as being broken.

Don't put yourself down.

Don't consider yourself to be unworthy just because you have scars.

Pay attention to your internal dialogue, and when you notice yourself criticizing your body, try to replace the negative comments with something positive. And if there are people in your life who are making you feel insecure about your body, try to distance yourself from these people. If your partner or spouse is making comments about your scars or having trouble accepting the new you, don't be afraid to verbalize how this hurts you.

My family has always been very open, and since I have two daughters, they've grown up coming in and out of my room while I was getting dressed. After my surgeries, I was worried about how they would react to my scars, but I didn't make a big deal out of it and it's been a non-issue. While my husband was only kind and loving toward my new body, it wasn't about him, it was about me. I had to make peace with the changes. I had to learn to love the new me.

Remember, what we look like on the outside isn't as important as who we are on the inside. Over time, it is my hope you fully accept yourself for who you are, scars and all. You fought hard to get your scars. You are a warrior. Don't forget it.

TIP 31: YOU AREN'T WHAT HAPPENED TO YOU

Don't define yourself by your illness. You are not cancer. You are not what you had or what happened to you. It can be hard to understand this, especially if you've been spending all your time dealing with cancer or if you're reminded of it every time you look in the mirror. Yes, it is part of your story, but your life is about so much more than your illness. Cancer can make you feel like it owns you. It can seep into everything, and you might even forget who you were or what life felt like before cancer. Take what you learn on your journey and carry it with you into your future. Let your lessons be the catalyst to helping you enjoy and make the most of your life. You must accept the changes in your body and move on. You are not your scars and you are absolutely not damaged goods. Make sure you remember this always.

TIP 32: 3D NIPPLE TATTOOS

So many people have asked me about this process, I thought I would address it here. Yes, I have 3D nipple tattoos. If you're wondering what this even means, it means the nipples on my breasts look real. Yep, it's true. I went to Paul, part of the Vinnie Myers team in Finksburg, Maryland. These amazing artists specialize in this procedure and I was blessed to get to do it. It helped me make peace with my body and accept the changes I've gone through. Now when I get out of the shower and look in the mirror, I don't think about cancer. Although things don't look perfect, I don't give it any thought. When I got the tattoos, I wasn't searching for perfection. I was hoping to normalize things and I got what I wanted.

Everyone is different and you have to figure out what you need to do to help yourself make peace with the changes in your body. You might not even care. But if you do, and there are things you can do to help yourself come to terms with the changes in your body, do them. Be willing to help yourself. Be patient with your body and recognize it might take a little time to get it where you want it to be. By the way, if you decide to seek out someone to do tattoos, make sure you go to someone who specializes in this particular art. There are many issues to be considered, and I can't say enough about the Vinnie Myers team. (If my kids are reading this and they're cringing because I just shared this information with the world, please remember I told you to skip this chapter. You should have listened.)

TRIBE TIP

Please, please, please watch what you say about the changes in the survivor's physical appearance. This is a very sensitive issue for a lot of people. If you aren't sure how a comment will be received, you're probably better off not saying anything. If you're having trouble dealing with the changes in your friend or family member's physical appearance, talk to someone other than the survivor. Be helpful and build the person up.

You can keep living life
the way you've always lived it
or you can have
the courage to go do what
you've always wanted to do.
Time is going to pass
either way.
It's your life, your time.

CHAPTER 19

CANCER CHANGED ME

I saw a lot on my journey, and afterward I realized I had changed. What I wanted out of life, how I wanted to spend my time and who I wanted to spend it with had all been transformed. I had a decision to make: I could go back to the way my life had been "BC," or I could have the courage to alter my path. It was one thing to say, "I'm a changed person," but it took fortitude to make decisions that reflected how I now viewed my life. I've always believed in the saying, "If you keep doing what you've always done you're going to get what you've always gotten." I didn't want to keep doing what I had always done. It was time to move forward and embrace the changed me.

I wanted to live my life fully and without regret. I didn't want to wait to do what I'd always dreamed of doing, I wanted to start following my dreams now. I was one of the lucky ones and I felt I had been given a second chance at life. I didn't want to waste it.

After deciding I didn't just want to let life happen to me, I wanted to actively make choices that were in line with my priorities, I refused to give into the fear that sometimes kept me up at night. I pushed myself forward. I learned to be patient with myself and gave myself time to process everything I had been through. I became my own best friend instead of my worst enemy. Getting through my cancer treatment had given me the courage to live my life the way I truly wanted to live it.

Hearing the words "You have cancer" made me realize I wasn't going to live forever. Of course, I'd always known this, but nothing says "Life is short" like a cancer diagnosis. I finally understood how valuable my time was and I decided I didn't want to waste one single day of my life. Even if I was truly blessed and lived to the ripe old age of 100, which no one that I know of in my family has done, my time on Earth would still be limited. I can't control how long I live, but I can control how I spend my time.

Time isn't a renewable resource. Most people don't think about this, but once it's gone, it's gone. And here's the really tricky part, we don't know how much time we have. It's the ultimate secret. Some of us will get to meet our grandchildren and some of us won't. It's a sobering thought. I was 42 when I was diagnosed and I wasn't ready to hit the eject button from Earth. I had a lot I still wanted to do.

Before cancer, I thought I was making the best decisions for my family, career and self. I just knew I had this life thing figured out. I know now I didn't. As long as I can remember, I've always been the type of person who rushed from one activity to another. I thought that's what busy, successful people did: they hurried. At the end of the day they had a lot to show for their time. I tended to move through life with a "full speed ahead" attitude, frantically checking things off my to-do list. A good day was when I didn't have any-thing left on my list. Back then, I didn't savor the moment I was in. How could I? I was too busy thinking about everything I had to do, all the places I needed to be. I was efficient and had big goals. I didn't like to miss anything and hated saying "no" to fun plans. I ran from one activity to the next. Instead of enjoying my present moment, I was thinking about the future and what would come next.

I thought nothing could or would derail me.

Cancer had other plans for me.

After going through my treatment plan and getting to the other side, one of the first things I did was quit my job. It didn't feed my soul and I just couldn't see myself going back to it. While I had loved it when I did it, being a financial advisor and thinking about money all day didn't excite me. I had always wanted to focus on my writing and now was the time to do it. I started Crazy Perfect Life and found my voice. I wanted to share my story and pour my soul out in words I hoped would help people dealing with their own challenges.

I have learned how to be intentional with my time. Each week, on Sunday, I take a little time to think through the week ahead. This helps me stay organized and plan what I need to do. It also allows me to make sure I'm spending my time doing the things that are important to me. Sure, I have plenty of responsibilities, just like you, but when I'm intentional about how I spend my time, there's room for everything. Have you ever heard someone say, "I wish I could do that but I don't have the time?" News flash: The time is there. If they really wanted to do whatever it was, they could find a way. It's all about priorities and setting aside the time to do what you want.

I'm not very interested in how much I can get done in a day anymore. I don't really care about my to-do list. The thought of multitasking seems exhausting and my priorities have completely changed. Cancer gave me the courage to live life on my own terms and it is freeing.

Another important change I made is who I spend my time with. My family has always been my priority, but I became more intentional with the interactions I have with the people I love. Especially my kids. I think about how we could have fun together, being silly and just letting the day take us where it will. I stopped being as structured and loosened up with them. We laugh more now, we aren't as serious and life feels lighter. I'm less concerned with how clean their rooms are and more concerned with the interactions and conversations we have with one another. That doesn't mean we don't argue. I have two teenage daughters! It just means I make sure we connect with one another as often as possible in a meaningful way.

We're also more focused on making sure we have family time. There is always something two teens could be doing with someone else, but we make our time together a priority. Just like I'm willing to miss a party or say "no" to certain plans, we insist they do the same if we've planned something as a family. My daughters haven't always embraced our "family fun," but I know in my heart it's the right thing to do.

"Do we have to?" they sometimes ask, hoping we'll cave in.

"Yes," we reply. "When you're the parents you can do what you want, but right now we're in charge."

They usually end up being happy spending time as a family and enjoy whatever it is we've asked them to do with us. I'm not being mean, I'm making sure I'm spending my time intentionally. If I didn't insist on setting time aside for us, life would get in the way and family time would never happen. One day, when my daughters are older and more mature, I hope they cherish the memories we've made together.

I have stopped worrying about what other people think of me and started really listening to the little voice inside my head, the one that knows what I truly want to do. I am really good at saying "no." I don't have to do everything, please everyone, or even get all the items on my to-do list checked off before going to bed. Nothing bad happens if I go to sleep with an incomplete list.

This intentional slowing down is what has made the magic really happen. I have discovered the joy of focusing on my here and now. I think less about the past and don't worry about the future. My eyes are open to what is going on around me and I try to notice everything.

Why is it so hard to just stay present?

To live in the moment?

Have you ever been in your car driving somewhere, then looked up and realized you were at your destination but didn't know how you got there? It's like someone else was driving. You're paying enough attention to the road to be safe, but your mind is elsewhere. When I'm practicing yoga, sometimes my mind starts wandering away from my current pose to what I'm going to make for dinner or what errands I need to run when I'm done. I don't even realize I'm thinking about something else until it's time to go into a new pose and I can't remember which leg to bring forward. When this happens, I laugh because it's a good reminder to me of how easy it is to forget to pay attention to what I'm actually doing. If this sounds like you, don't worry. Many people travel through their life thinking about what they have to do next or what they've already done. Most of us don't focus on what we're doing when we're actually doing it.

That's what living with intention is all about: giving your full attention to what you're currently doing and creating time for what makes you happy. It seems so simple, right? That's because it is. We're the ones who make it hard.

We all have responsibilities and things we must do. However, when you actively start deciding how you want to spend your time, you can absolutely make time for what is truly important to you. Trust me, you'll feel a lot happier when you start managing your time this way.

You also need to give yourself permission to spend a little time each day by yourself. It's important to have time to connect with your thoughts, to sit and think about your life, or maybe meditate. You need to make this a priority, even if it's just 15 minutes a day. Whenever I have time alone, I bask in it. It usually involves a hot cup of tea and my journal.

Making time for yourself isn't frivolous or selfish, it's necessary. It's where you can process what you've been through and grow. If you don't think you have time for a little solitude, or feel guilty about taking this time, you're denying yourself the opportunity to discover the real you. I encourage you to intentionally schedule alone time every week. And maybe, just maybe, when your day starts to go in a thousand directions, or you start to feel anxious or worried, you can close your eyes, take a deep breath and return to your quiet time. It will ground you and help you feel peaceful. Learning to use meditation and focusing on your breathing can have a positive impact on your body and lower your stress level. I try to spend at least 15-30 minutes each day on this. It feels great, helps me relax and I find I have more patience and feel calmer.

We can worry about what might or might not happen in the future, we can focus on the past, but all we really have is now.

TIP 33: DON'T MAKE DRASTIC CHANGES IMMEDIATELY

You might find yourself wanting to make some big changes in your life after you go through cancer. This is normal because your priorities have probably shifted a bit. However, don't rush into anything. Sit with whatever big changes you're considering for a few months to make sure it's really what you want to do. I'm all about being spontaneous, but you've been through a lot and this probably isn't the best time to make impulsive decisions. If you want to buy that red convertible and cruise around town, great, go for it. Just make sure it's what you really want to do before you cash in your savings account. You've been through enough, you don't need to add regretful decisions to the list.

TIP 34: BE INTENTIONAL ABOUT HOW YOU SPEND YOUR TIME

Be careful with how you spend your time and who you spend it with. Intentionally making decisions regarding your time will ensure you're using it well. Don't go through life on auto-pilot, assuming you have all the time in the world. Pay attention to what you're doing every day.

Don't waste your time worrying about your mortality. Instead of fearing death, be afraid you aren't living your best life and do something about it. Step out of your comfort zone and go after whatever it is you dream of doing with your life. A cancer diagnosis can cause a person to wake up and see things differently. Be willing to listen to the voice inside your head that might be pushing you forward. No one knows how long their lives will be, but you can make the most of each day you're blessed to have.

TIP 35: BE PRESENT

Commit to living in the present moment. When you're with your family and friends, look at them and pay attention when someone is talking to you. Ditch the electronics. Seriously. Put your phone away. If you're watching a movie, just watch the movie. If you're having coffee with a friend, just talk. Nothing is more frustrating to me than when I'm trying to connect with my daughters and they're constantly looking at their phones instead of paying attention to what I'm saying. It makes me crazy, not in a good way.

Remember, you don't have to multitask. There's no award for the person who does the most in a given day. Try to enjoy what you're doing and you'll find yourself feeling happier, more relaxed and content.

TIP 36: BE PATIENT WITH YOUR FRIENDS AND FAMILY

Don't be surprised if everyone in your life doesn't understand how cancer has changed you. After you've completed your treatment plan, most people will assume you will go back to how your life was before you were diagnosed. They might not get why you want to do things differently or be as supportive as you'd like. You may hear things such as, "You've changed a lot," "You're different now," or, my favorite, "I don't recognize who you are anymore." That's OK. They don't have to understand everything.

It's hard to fully comprehend what it feels like to go through cancer unless you've personally experienced it. To others, you went through an illness and you're cured now. They might not understand you can't just flip a switch and be "all better," or that you might be struggling with your mortality and the fear that often accompanies the "Big C." Try to be patient with your friends and family. Remember, you're the person who has changed, not them, and they might not like all the changes you've made because it might cause them to see things in their own lives they aren't happy with. You never know.

TRIBE TIP

Don't take it personally if the survivor wants to spend time alone each day. Remember, they've been through a lot and are still processing things. Give them the time and space they need to figure things out for themselves. When they spend time alone, they aren't choosing to not be with you or rejecting you, they're just wanting a little solitude. Try to understand the emotional impact cancer has on a person, the fear it can cause and the thoughts they've been struggling with. Your loved one is learning how to live as a survivor. Spending time alone will help.

Living with
gratitude can be
the difference
between living in
black and white
versus living in
color.

CHAPTER 20

FIND GRATITUDE AND HOLD ON TO IT WITH BOTH HANDS

I've always been a relatively polite person. If asked, people who know me would most likely agree I have good manners. I say "please," "thank you" and "you're welcome" on a regular basis. But just because I'm courteous doesn't mean I live with gratitude. In fact, living a life of gratitude wasn't something I ever thought about until I went through cancer. It was the hard days that taught me to be thankful for all the blessings in my life. Being able to recognize the good in your life, even when you're going through a challenging experience, is important. It's also something you get to decide. Living with gratitude is a choice.

Taking the time to open your eyes to the blessings that surround you, even when things are rough, will help you get through whatever you're dealing with because it's affirming. It helps to recognize no matter what you're facing, you still have good in your life and there is much to be grateful for. I wish I had learned this earlier, it would have added a richness to my life I didn't even know was missing. But instead of feeling bad about not doing it sooner, I'm glad to have discovered it now.

When we're facing a challenge, it can be difficult to find something to be grateful for. If life seems overwhelming, the last thing you want to do is count your blessings. I understand, I've been there. But what I've learned from the hard times in my life is it actually feels good to count your blessings, even when you're struggling to get through the day. It's important to remember there is almost always at least one reason to give thanks.

I'm sure more than once you've heard someone say, "I didn't know what I had until it was gone." Why is this? Why don't we appreciate what we have when it's right in front of us? Why do we have to lose someone or something before we fully recognize how lucky we were to actually have them or it in the first place? Is it because we're too consumed with the details of life? Do we assume the people and things in our lives will always be there? Do we expect everything to be perfect and when it isn't, turn our backs to the blessings we're fortunate to have?

It's not easy to do, but I can't stress how much better you will feel if you start taking the time to notice all the blessings in your life. Try to just be thankful for today and the fact that you're alive. You might not like everything about your current situation, but there is always something to be thankful for, regardless of what you're facing.

Cancer helped me to understand how important it is to be grateful for all the wonderful things in my life. I learned to not take my life for granted. To stop assuming the blessings in my life would always be there. For the first time in my life, I started seeing all the good things in front of me. I recognized how lucky I was just to wake up each morning and be alive, to have people in my life who loved and cared for me. I started noticing what was around me—the beautiful sunset, the pretty flowers, the birds chirping in the morning. I stopped expecting the good in my life to always be there and instead felt blessed to have it.

It's easy to get a picture in your mind of how your life should be, but I don't know many people whose lives are exactly as they planned. It doesn't mean you don't have a great life, it just means there was a deviation in the plan, and that's OK. Instead of thinking about what didn't happen, what you don't have, or the hardships that have been tossed your way, look at all of the positives. Focusing on what you feel is lacking can make you bitter and angry. You don't need that in your life. Remember, our thoughts have a significant impact on the way we feel. Spend your time and energy being grateful by focusing on all the good you have in your life. If you tend to forget or overlook the blessings, keep a daily list of what you're grateful for.

I like to write in my journal when my family is still sleeping and I'm drinking a cup of hot tea. I sit in my kitchen with my dog, Winnie, and scribble down all I'm thankful for in that moment. Sometimes I have a lot of things to write. Other times, if life is feeling complicated and I'm dealing with a difficult challenge, I might struggle to think of even a few. I usually try to come up with at least three things. My mental list of what I'm grateful for often occurs before I get out of bed in the morning, or even as I'm falling asleep the night before. I think about my day and what made me happy, and that's what I write down the next morning. I've trained my mind to automatically notice the blessings in my life and the good things that have happened to me. I love this about myself, and it can happen to you too. It just takes time and patience.

The more I've practiced this exercise, the easier it's gotten for my mind to go to a place of gratitude throughout my entire day. I tend to notice the beauty around me, the positive aspects of my life and the good that comes my way. This brings me a great deal of joy.

I don't take it for granted that I'm here and able to watch my daughters grow up. I understand this isn't something every parent gets to do. In fact, I've met people who weren't as lucky as I am, and in some ways I feel I owe it to them to fully appreciate all the blessings in my life. Cancer showed me that just being with my family is a true blessing. Food tastes better, my interactions with people are more meaningful and the conversations I have with others tend to be deeper and more authentic.

I used to dread running errands. I viewed it as a complete nuisance and waste of time. I would try to finish whatever it was I needed to do as quickly as possible. Now when I'm running errands, I try to be present and enjoy it. I know what it feels like to not be able to go to the grocery store because my white blood cell count was too low, so now it doesn't seem so bad. In fact, I'm always amazed at the interactions I have with strangers when I'm out and about. I relish the unplanned connection, the opportunity to learn from someone or see things a different way.

I've learned to live life as a grateful person, and that has made my life richer. As I was writing this chapter, I decided to go back and look at my journal entries from when I was diagnosed through my treatment plan. I didn't live with a lot of gratitude back then. I had just started trying to learn how to live a life of thankfulness and it was very difficult. I've already shared with you that I wasn't a ray of sunshine, and those were some of the hardest days of my life. Looking back at my journal, here's an example of the things I listed during that time:

I'm grateful to have my family.

I'm grateful to not be nauseous right now.

I'm grateful for Netflix.

It's pretty obvious where I was and how much I was struggling. But I was learning how to be thankful, even in dark times. I was training myself to see the glass half full. I felt so unhappy and sorry for myself during that time period, I struggled with finding gratitude. Looking at my list now, I can see a difference in my approach. This is a direct result of the changes I've experienced since I went through cancer. I've grown a lot over the past few years and my list reflects it.

You'll be amazed at how taking the time to really notice the good in your life, to savor and appreciate it, will bring more good. We attract what we think about.

Regardless of what you're facing, recognize the many gifts you're fortunate enough to have. Living with gratitude can be the difference between living in black and white versus living in color. It will make your life richer, brighter and more vivid.

Sometimes we look for really big things to be thankful for when we take the time to count our blessings. We acknowledge the grand things in our life. Maybe it's a new job, a new member of your family or something else extra special. These things are easy to identify when we talk about feeling grateful. But what about the little things? The daily blessings we have in our lives that are easy to overlook? It's not often we have big events in our lives. That's why it's important to find little things to feel happy about every day. You might be worried about your job, but you have a job. You might be bickering with your significant other, but you have a significant other to bicker with. Your kids might be driving you crazy, but you're blessed to have them. You might be stressed about getting the results back from a medical exam, but you're lucky to have a professional team to help you.

Life isn't perfect, so don't expect it to be. You're just setting yourself up to be let down if you do. It doesn't come in a perfectly wrapped package with a beautiful bow. It's messy and made up of thousands of different moments. Some are good. Some are better. Some seriously suck. When I was being treated for cancer and feeling pretty bad, it was hard to remember I wouldn't always feel sick from the side effects. I needed a big dose of perspective. Consider this your dose of perspective: Nothing lasts forever. Unfortunately, this also holds true for the wonderful parts of life, the times we want to go on forever because we're so happy. If we don't take the time to acknowledge the positive moments in life, we'll miss them. And no one wants to miss the good stuff.

TIP 37: FOCUS ON WHAT YOU HAVE

I get how hard your days might be right now and how easy it is to have a pity party. I've definitely had my share of those. But if you focus on what you don't have, what's lacking in your life, how you were dealt an unfair hand and how nothing is going well for you,

you won't be helping yourself. Instead, think about what you do have, what is working and how lucky you are. Yes, I said lucky. Even if you're dealing with cancer, there are things in your life you're fortunate to have. They might be hard to find, but they're there. Be willing to take the time to look for the blessings in your life.

For example, do you have people in your life to help take care of you, support you and talk with? Are you receiving medical care? Do you have doctors who care about you and a medical team you trust? Do you have medication to take, a comfortable place to rest and entertainment to distract you? These are all things to be thankful for.

Here's how you start feeling grateful for what you have in your life: Sit and think about what you like about your life, what is working and what makes you happy. Write down three things you feel grateful for right now in your journal or on a sheet of paper. If you struggle with this a little bit, be patient. If you've been feeling sorry for yourself for a while and have been thinking nothing in your life is going well, it might take a little time to train your mind to look at things in a more positive way.

Take the time to do this each morning, before you start your day, and watch how it positively impacts you. Write whatever comes to mind, whatever you're grateful for. Don't judge what you write or label it as "good" or "bad." The fact that you're doing this is good. Period.

TIP 38: QUIT COMPLAINING

Seriously. If something happens that you don't like, every time you complain about it you give it power. Focusing on it isn't going to make things better, it'll bring you down. Stop complaining and start doing.

For example, let's say you're having a rough day. You feel tired and depressed and you don't have any energy. You're worn out and just want to stay in bed all day and bask in your yuckiness. Whenever you talk to a friend or family member on the phone and they ask you how you are, you talk about how awful you feel, how exhausted you are and how you're tired of feeling sick. Since you're probably talking to at least a couple people each day, you keep repeating the same negative story over and over. How are you helping yourself? You aren't. In fact, you're feeding the yuckiness by focusing on it. You are certainly entitled to feel this way, but thinking about it and talking about it won't make you feel any better.

Instead, spend that energy helping yourself figure out ways to feel better. If you're really tired, take several naps throughout the day. However, try to limit the amount of time you stay in bed. Move to a different place in your house, such as a den, living room or sunroom. Changing your scenery will help you feel better. If the weather is nice, consider sitting outside for a little while every day and even taking short walks. Take a shower or warm bath and change your clothes. If you've been laying around in your PJs or robe, consider getting dressed. Even if you just put on another clean pair of PJs, it is sure to make you feel better. Focus on your nutrition and make sure you're eating lots of healthy foods to give your body the nutrients it needs. Drink lots of hot tea, eat warm soups or anything else that soothes you. Find activities you enjoy doing around your house. Watch movies, sew, do an art project or read an inspirational book or article.

Instead of spending your day feeling sorry for yourself, do something to help yourself feel better. Don't focus on what you don't have or don't like, think about what you do have and what is going well. There is always something positive in your life.

Find it.

Hold onto it with both hands.

Help yourself.

TIP 39: FINDING GRATITUDE IN THE HARDEST SEASON OF LIFE

If you're facing an advanced cancer situation and you find yourself struggling with your future and how much time you have left, I'm so sorry. I can only imagine how difficult this is and my heart goes out to you and your family. Here's my advice to you. Instead of thinking about your future and what might or might not happen, try to focus on how you're spending your time each day. Commit to being present. Recognize you have a choice. You can give into the fear and worry, or you can make the most of each day. Show up to your life, right now. Try to recognize your blessings, even in this difficult season, and be patient with yourself.

TRIBE TIP

Living a life of gratitude is beneficial for everyone. You don't need to be a cancer survivor to practice acknowledging and appreciating all the good you have in your life. I encourage you to start a daily gratitude journal for yourself. It can be hard to watch a friend or family member go through cancer. You're probably feeling a little down yourself, even if he or she has finished treatments and survived. By giving yourself a way to recognize the blessings in your life, you will be helping yourself stay positive.

Life isn't perfect, but
it's worth fighting for.
There's beauty all around you.
Choose joy. Be positive.
Take the time to connect
with the people who
mean the most to you.
Guard your time.
Believe in yourself.
Expect good things.

CHAPTER 21

START BEING A JOY SEEKER

One of the benefits of living a life of thanks and being grateful for everything you have is how it makes you feel. It feels wonderful to take stock of everything around you and it gives you a heightened level of happiness. I never understood what it meant to feel joyful until I started taking the time to count my blessings. Now, on most days, I wake up excited to be alive. I no longer take life for granted.

After my cancer experience, I became a joy seeker. I changed my mindset to focus on what I had, not what was lacking. Being a joy seeker means you look at each day as an opportunity to create and live your best life. It changes the way you view everything around you.

Before cancer, I didn't enjoy my life as much as I do now. For example, whenever I exercised, I used to think of it as a means to an end. I was focused on burning calories and just getting it done. I can't tell you how many beautiful sunny days I spent inside on a treadmill because I wanted to maximize my workout. Now, while I still exercise to stay healthy, I'm more concerned with enjoying the experience. I love being outdoors and connecting with nature. I'll choose walking outside over running on a treadmill any day. It makes me happy, and I'm all about maximizing my happiness each day.

This doesn't mean my life is perfect. I still get grumpy sometimes, just ask my kids. But I tend to shake off life's little annoyances faster than I used to. I keep the big picture top of mind. I know there are always going to be things in my life I don't like, but as a joy seeker, I actively spend my time and energy on what I like about my life and what is working. I make sure I do at least one activity each day that makes me really happy. There are days that are more hectic than others, and I don't have as much time as I would like, but I make sure I have at least a little fun budgeted into each day of my life. Some days, if I have a lot of time, I'll meet a friend for a long lunch or go to an exercise class I've been wanting to try. I might slow down and have a really great conversation with my kids or go on a spontaneous trip for ice cream. Other days I treat myself to a coffee in between meetings or driving my kids around. Once you become a joy seeker, you start to think of ways you can make everything you do more special.

Before cancer I didn't pay much attention to this. Making sure I had fun each day wasn't really on my radar. I was too busy thinking about my goals and what I needed to do to accomplish them. Don't get me wrong, I still have big dreams and work very hard, I just make sure there's a little fun laced into each day. Not only does this make me happier, it also makes me work better because I've taken the time to care for my spirit, to honor myself. Plus, since I'm doing work that is in line with what truly matters to me, it doesn't really feel like work. I'm very grateful for this.

My family has noticed this change in me and it's carried over onto them. Recently, on the way to the movies, I said to my husband, "You know what would make this moment really special?"

"What is it this time?" Jon said with playful sarcasm. "What would make this moment really special?"

I could tell he was intrigued.

"What if we stopped and got coffee and took it into the theater?"

My husband rolled his eyes and laughed. We ended up not having time to grab the coffee, which is probably a good thing because I'm not sure we would have been allowed to bring it in with us. But it's taking the time to make ordinary moments special and fun that brings me a lot of joy. I see my daughters doing this each day too and it makes me happy.

It's enjoyable for me to look for ways to spread the joy and celebrate with my family. I don't need a big occasion to have a special family dinner, host a luncheon for my friends or take an opportunity to recognize something one of my daughters has done. Making ordinary moments special is fun for everyone.

Here's the really cool part. Anyone can become a joy seeker. Yes, even you. You might be thinking, "This sounds like something I'd like to try. How can I become a joy seeker?" It's really quite simple. It's all in how you look at your life.

You grasp life with both hands and insist on living the way you truly want to live. You don't hold back. You don't wait. You don't dismiss the good things. You refuse to let anyone stop you, shut you down, convince you whatever you want to do won't work, or tell you your dreams don't matter. A joy seeker is someone who is positive and uplifting. That doesn't mean they don't face hard times or difficult challenges. They have struggles and problems, just like everyone else does. But they choose to make every day count. They decide to do the best they can with what they've been given. They don't dwell on what isn't working or what they don't like about their current situation. They don't give in to life's little annoyances or chase drama.

Joy seekers see the glass as half full instead of half empty. They go after happiness and don't give in when life gets rough. A joy seeker understands who they spend time with can have a direct impact on how they feel, so they surround themselves with positive people who make them feel good, who lift them up instead of bringing them down. They manage their expectations and know how to find magical moments when life is hard. They are joy seekers even when it isn't easy, especially when it isn't easy.

I'm going to tell you a secret. Are you listening? This is important. Your opinion really does matter. Not my opinion, not your family's opinion, or even your doctor's opinion. What you think about your circumstances and how you view your life will directly impact you. If you think your life sucks and nothing is going your way, you're right. If you view life as hard and impossible, it will be. If you think your cancer is going to get the best of you, and there's no way you can survive, you're probably going to be right. This can be empowering if you choose to use this knowledge to your advantage by managing your thoughts and steering yourself toward a positive outlook.

Let's take it a step further. Perhaps your doctor has given you statistics that aren't in your favor. Remember, statistics don't directly have anything to do with you because they don't take into consideration your specific situation (or your kick-ass attitude). You have two choices: you can think about the statistics and percentages all the time, dwell on them and give up, or you can decide you're going to be the person who defies the odds and crushes cancer. The same holds true if the statistics are in your favor. They still don't have anything to do directly with you. Yes, it's easier to believe you're going to be OK when the numbers are in your favor, but your thoughts still impact your overall health. Don't dismiss the power of your mind or the benefits of being positive. This is where the mantra we talked about before comes into play. Hopefully you now have a mantra you find uplifting. If not, go back and reread that chapter!

I wasn't always a joy seeker. It was something I learned to be the hard way. Sometimes I think the universe sends us challenging times to teach us lessons. It's what we do with these lessons that can positively transform us or push us backward. I could have let myself spiral down into a dark hole, given in to the "why me?" attitude and wallowed in my sadness. That wouldn't have served me well, and I'm glad I didn't. I wouldn't be living my life to the fullest and making the most of every single day if I had allowed my bad attitude to stick around. If you've been through a hard time, faced a challenging situation, felt so low you didn't think you would ever survive, or if you're currently going through this now, consider this a gentle reminder to push yourself forward.

Don't give up.

You are strong, even if you don't think you are. You have greatness inside of you, even if you doubt yourself. Maybe you just need to hear it. If so, I'm happy to be the one to tell you. In fact, it's my honor. I hope you decide right now to live the rest of your life being positive. Intentionally make that choice. Commit right now to being a joy seeker. Look for ways to make your life better every day, even in difficult situations.

An important part of life is having fun. You know, that three-letter word that symbolizes laughter and smiles, good times and playfulness? Here's a serious question, and I want you to think about it. Are you having fun in your life? Do you even remember what it feels like to have fun? If you can't remember the last time you enjoyed yourself, we might be in trouble, but that's OK, I like a challenge.

After I went through cancer, I realized I wanted to have more fun in my life. I wanted to laugh more. To be less serious and more flexible. To be open to all the wonderful opportunities life has to offer and to make the time to fit in the things I really wanted to do. It's easy to let responsibilities and schedules get in the way of having fun once you're an adult. Having a mortgage or a stack of bills to pay can suck the playfulness right out of life. We get so caught up in the day-to-day madness, who has time to even think about having fun? Consider this a little reminder: You deserve to have some fun in your life. You deserve to laugh. You deserve to enjoy yourself and look forward to doing whatever it is that brings you joy.

Even if you were diagnosed with cancer.

Even if you feel like you're spending your days going to doctor's appointments.

Even if you have a to-do list that's so long you don't think it will ever get finished.

Before you can have some fun, you've got to figure out what it is that's preventing you from having it in the first place. It takes courage to admit you don't like something in your life, and even greater courage to actually do something about it. When we aren't true to ourselves or living an authentic life, it's obvious. We feel it every day and can only pretend otherwise for so long. If you're getting out of bed each day filled with dread, you need to take a close look at what's going on. Nothing in this life is perfect, but you deserve to get up in the morning feeling excited about the day. If you aren't happy, figure out what you need to do to get there, and do it.

It's by taking the time to ask questions of ourselves that we find the answers. Don't sugar-coat things. Be real. You can't live your best life if you aren't willing to be honest about your current one, and you can't change anything if you aren't aware of what you'd like to be different. It's worth taking the time to figure this out. After all, it's your life we're talking about.

If you feel happy and content, count your blessings. Recognize it's a gift to feel satisfied with who you are and where you are in your life. Don't take it for granted. Happiness isn't guaranteed. We must work at it, figure out what we need and create it. It's an obtainable goal for me and for you.

TIP 40: DO SOMETHING EVERY DAY THAT MAKES YOU HAPPY

The key to really enjoying your life is to intentionally take the time to do things that make your life fulfilling. I understand it might be a little challenging to make the day special when you're rushing around, taking care of your kids, trying to get to work on time, or going to your doctor's office. However, that doesn't mean you can't find a little time each day to do something that puts a smile on your face. Go for a walk, take a yoga class, meet a friend for coffee or try a new restaurant. The options are endless. The only thing stopping you is you. It often doesn't take a lot of time or cost a lot of money to make the everyday moments of life special or to find something that puts a smile on your face. Don't get in your own way or shut down the opportunity to spend time doing something that brings you happiness. Allow yourself the time every day to do something you love. Make sure your life isn't just about fulfilling responsibilities or checking things off a list. You deserve so much more, don't you think? Go find the things that make you happy and allow yourself to become a joy seeker.

TRIBE TIP

Focus on ways you can bring a little joy into your own life. You might have spent a lot of time and energy taking care of a friend or family member who was dealing with cancer and your needs were pushed to the side. This can be draining, especially since cancer usually isn't a quick fix. It's time for you to give yourself a little extra dose of joy. Be the priority for a little while and find something that makes you happy.

Living is an art.
Mold your life into
the picture you want.
Give yourself the freedom to
figure out what direction
feels right.
Enjoy the process.
Create your masterpiece.

CHAPTER 22

WHAT'S YOUR PURPOSE OR PASSION?

After I finished my treatment plan, I felt lost. I was in between being a cancer patient and being back in the real world, and I didn't quite seem to fit in either place. I spent a lot of time taking long walks outside and thinking, trying to figure out how I wanted to spend my time and what my purpose was. I was happy and knew how lucky I was, but I struggled with what I wanted to do with the rest of my life.

Make sure you're living your best life and spending your time on things that feed your soul. Just because you expect to have a lot more tomorrows doesn't mean you should waste your today. You have to listen to what speaks to your heart and commit to doing it. No one can do this for you.

Living is an art I constantly work on. The more effort and energy I put into living the life I want, the more satisfied I am with the result. If something doesn't feel right, I try to find a different way to approach it. Every day we get a fresh start, another 24 hours to have a do-over. There are very few things in life that can't be changed.

You aren't the same person today you were a year ago, five years ago, or before you went through cancer. Our experiences and environment change and impact who we are. When we overcome difficult challenges, we gain inner strength and compassion for other people.

It can be challenging when we've changed and the life we're currently living doesn't fit who we've become. One way isn't better or worse than the other, you just might need to modify the way you're living to make sure it reflects who you've become. Growing pains can be uncomfortable, but you can push through them and get to the other side. Think how boring and monotonous life would be if we stayed stagnant over the course of our lifetimes.

People need to embrace who they really are or who they're meant to be. You have qualities inside you that make you wonderfully unique. When you share your talents and passions with the world, everyone benefits. Look at some of the great inventors, scholars, and movers and shakers of the past. Most were quirky and didn't conform. They made up their own rules as they went along. What they had was talent, a strong desire to be successful at what they believed in, and a passion to carry out whatever it was they were doing. They were brave souls who dared to live life on their own terms. When they failed, they didn't quit. They figured out a different way and tried again.

I started paying attention to what I gravitated toward and discovered it was writing. I had been wanting to focus on my writing for many years, but I never had the time because I was too busy doing everything else. While I was in my holding pattern—after I finished my treatment but before I was physically ready to go back to work—my mind would think about what I wanted to write, and I would get lost in my thoughts.

When I was initially diagnosed with cancer and was about to start chemo, my husband came home with a present for me.

"Open it," he said with a smile on his face.

Inside was a small laptop, one that would fit into a large purse.

"You've always wanted to have time to write," he said. "Maybe you can write while you're going through your treatments."

It was an incredibly thoughtful gesture, which I truly appreciated but didn't take advantage of right away. Right after my diagnosis, I didn't feel like doing much of anything, including writing. But then I was drawn to it, and it became a very important part of my survival and recovery.

Find something that causes time to slow down. An activity you become so engrossed in you don't realize how much time passes when you're doing it. Something that makes you feel completely focused and relaxed. That's how you know you've found the right thing. You'll never know what you love doing unless you give it a shot. It just might be the thing you've been waiting your whole life to discover.

If you're feeling unsettled, bored or restless, that's a sure sign you aren't pursuing your passions or living the life you want. You deserve to do something that makes you feel good. Something that excites you and brings you joy. Pay attention to how you feel.

Perhaps you're in a profession you never really wanted to go into in the first place. Maybe you ended up there because you were pleasing your parents. Or maybe it was the potential financial gains that profession would bring or the prestige it held. It's hard to find your passion when money, clout or another person's aspirations for you are the driving forces behind your decision.

If you find yourself questioning what you're doing and desiring something else, be willing to explore other options. Perhaps you've decided you want to help other people. You've been through a difficult experience and survived, so you want to help those who are facing a similar situation. If you find you want to change your focus but you can't leave your job, don't worry, there are always options. Think about using some of your free time to feed your passion. There are many organizations that would love to have your help as a volunteer. Don't just think about giving back, find a way. Pick up the phone and make the call. Go online and look for opportunities. When we help other people, not only are we providing assistance and inspiration to others, it comes back to us in the form of pure joy. Try it, I think you'll like it.

If you aren't ready to make a huge change, think about how you can bring your new interests into your current life. The important thing is you're willing to give yourself the space to decide what you truly feel passionate about and find a way to spend time doing it. If you make a mistake, learn from it and put it behind you. Don't dwell on it. Don't beat yourself up over it. And, whatever you do, don't give up.

I find the more effort and energy I put into creating the life I want, the more satisfied I am with what I'm getting out of it. If something doesn't feel right, I try to find a different way to approach it. If you aren't happy with the direction your life is headed or the choices you've made, don't just give in and assume things have to stay the way they are. Instead, dare to mix things up a little bit.

Remember, living takes work, practice and patience. We all have to erase a few lines or even draw a whole new picture sometimes before we get it right. The only way to get what you want out of life is to put the time and energy into figuring it out.

Don't get frustrated.

Don't give up.

Don't quit.

I like immediate gratification. I can be impatient, and when I decide I want something to happen, I want it to happen now. However, life doesn't work this way. You have to work toward a goal, one day at a time, and keep yourself focused on the end result. Most importantly, you have to expect little bumps along the way and be willing to keep forging ahead. Figure out what you want to do, what your goals are, and start tackling them one step at a time, one day at a time. Nothing is sweeter than the taste of success that comes from hard work. It will feel so good when you figure out how you want to spend your time and find a way to make it happen.

When you've found something that you feel passionate about and you allow yourself the time to do it, you will be content. You'll get out of bed excited about the day ahead of you and all the fun things you have to look forward to. That's how I felt when I started writing. I knew it was what I wanted to do, I just had to figure out how to make it fit into my life. Don't get frustrated if you don't know what you want out of your life. Let yourself explore different hobbies and interests and eventually something will strike you just right and you'll know. Trust your instincts. Have fun with it and enjoy the process of self-discovery.

TIP 41: HELP YOURSELF HAVE A GOOD DAY

The saying, "The way you start is the way you finish," is true. There are things you can do each morning to help yourself have a good day.

1. Set your alarm and get up – Decide the night before what time you need to get up, making sure you give yourself plenty of time to do whatever you need to do in the morning. Here's the hard part: when your alarm goes off, you actually need to get out of bed. I know it can be painful. I'm not a morning person, and this is seriously difficult for me, but oversleeping is actually worse in the long run. Remember this when you want nothing more than to hit the snooze button and give yourself another 20 minutes of beauty rest. All the beauty rest in the world isn't going to help if you have mascara running down your face and have on different shoes because you didn't have time to get ready properly.

2. Have some quiet time – Take a little time each morning to sit with your thoughts, read something inspirational or write in a journal. It doesn't have to be a lot of time. Even 15 minutes of quiet time can have a significant, positive impact on your day. I like to write in my journal in the morning, sometimes while I'm still in bed. You might prefer to make yourself a cup of coffee or tea and sit in your favorite chair while you take a few moments to wake up, or read inspirational material on your patio. The options are endless. Figure out what works for you and do it every morning.

3. Be organized – If you know you need to have certain items ready in the morning, pack them the night before. There's nothing more stressful than not being able to find what you need and knowing the clock is ticking. I can't begin to count the number of times I've rushed around like a crazy woman searching for my keys. Have you ever done this? It's not a great way to start the day. Don't forget about the food you'll need, including healthy snacks. You can even pick out your clothing the night before. Anything you can do to help yourself have a calm morning is a good thing.

4. Establish a routine – You might like to shower in the morning, exercise before you go to work or eat a healthy breakfast. Try various things until you find a routine that works for you. You might have family members you need to assist, children who need your help or pets to take care of. A structured routine is the best way to stay organized and on track. With a little planning, you'll be able to manage your morning responsibilities and carve out a little time for yourself.

5. Expect to have a good day – Look at the day ahead of you with appreciation and joy. Expect your day to play out positively. Even if you have a meeting you don't want to attend or a doctor's appointment you're dreading, expect it to go well. If you have a positive outlook going into your day, you're more likely to actually have a good day.

TIP 42: BE WILLING TO FAIL

When we fail, there is rarely any permanent damage done. Our egos might take a hit and we might have to swallow a bit of humble pie, but we get through it if we let ourselves. Don't let your fear of failure prevent you from taking chances. You can't succeed unless you try. You can't win if you aren't willing to play. Lighten up a bit and allow yourself the opportunity to explore new areas. Believe in yourself. When you move forward with an "I can" attitude, that's when the magic happens. Even if things don't go exactly how you wanted them to go, it's OK. Continue to build yourself up and cheer yourself on. Think about all the wonderful things the world never got to experience because people were afraid to fail. The world needs you to push through the fear and be willing to try.

The saying, "You'll never know if you don't try," is 100% accurate. If you don't try something, there's absolutely no way you can be successful at it. What's the worst that could happen? You try something and it doesn't work out. You give an idea your best shot and nothing goes the way you want it to. Big deal. You'll get over it. I've tried and failed at many things in my life. The funny thing is, I tend to forget the things that didn't work out. Sure, I might have felt disappointed and frustrated at the time, but I got over it, and so will you. Time has a way of lessening the blow and helping us gain perspective.

It's hard to step away from what other people want you to do and live off the grid. Here's the thing: You are the only one who knows what will feed your soul. You get one chance to create the life you want. Figure out a way to make it happen. Today. Embrace who you truly are, be your wonderful, unique self. You don't have to live your life struggling to fit in. You don't have to conform to the "right" way of doing things. Decide for yourself what you want out of life and how you want to spend your time. Then have the courage to follow your heart.

TRIBE TIP

You might notice changes in the survivor before he or she is even aware of them. If this is the case, be a source of encouragement and help the survivor go after his or her dreams. Help them figure out a way to discover what their passions are. Give them permission to take chances. Help them try to figure out what they want to do with their time, especially if they seem a little restless. Trying to go back to living life after cancer can be confusing, and your friend or family member will need your love and support through this transitional time.

Living with intention is about
focusing on your present
moment.
Don't wait.
**Have the courage to live
the life you truly want.**
Push yourself forward
instead of holding
yourself back.

CHAPTER 23

LIVE LIFE ON YOUR TERMS, NOW

How many times have you thought about something you really wanted to do, then talked yourself out of it? You convinced yourself you would do it later, tomorrow, next year. That there would be time in your future.

It's not hard to come up with reasons to stonewall a plan. We might think about something we yearn to do for a few days and vow to stop putting it off, then life gets in the way. We get distracted and forget about the promises we've made to ourselves. What we longed to do gets moved to the bottom of our list, or removed from the list completely. I have to admit, before cancer I did this a lot, especially once I became a mom. I assumed there would be lots of time in my future to do some of the things I always wanted to do. It wasn't hard to put my kids' needs before mine and tell myself I would do my stuff later.

It's easy for life to take us down a certain road and for us to never veer from it. I had majored in finance when I was in college and spent each summer working at large banking institutions. I longed to be a waitress, camp counselor or lifeguard. I wanted to do something fun, but was afraid of how a "fun" summer job on my resume would look to potential employers. When I graduated from college, I got a great first job in the banking industry and was on my way to a lifelong financial career. After working for several years in the retail side of the bank, then holding a few management positions, I landed in a training program to become an investment counselor. I was in my twenties and had an opportunity to make a lot of money doing something I was good at. All my hard work had paid off.

Yet sometimes, when I had free time, I would find myself writing stories and longing to write a book. "One day," I told myself, "I'll have time to sit in a coffee shop and write my heart out." This wasn't a pipe dream that appeared out of nowhere. In high school I had written for the school newspaper, and when I started college I convinced the campus newspaper to let a freshman finance major write articles. But I was encouraged to say the course in business and gave up writing after one article.

Before I was diagnosed, I felt lucky to have the job I had, and it wasn't hard to justify putting off writing. We all do this with lots of things: the trip that can wait until retirement, the new job that can wait until the kids grow up, the art class that can wait until we save a little more money. We move things into the "later" category and put off doing what we really want to do until the time is right. When we had our kids, I was in the thick of my job, with many clients and responsibilities, making a lot of money. Walking away from it didn't make sense. I was happy, my kids were happy and life was good. Sometimes, in the middle of the night when I couldn't sleep, I would hear my inner self say, "Quit your job, stay home with your kids and write." I would wake up the next morning thinking it was a crazy idea, and I quickly put it out of my head. After I went through cancer, I realized I didn't just want different things, I also didn't want to wait any longer. I couldn't see the point of putting off doing what I really wanted to do. I was seeing more clearly, and for the first time in my life I had the courage to go after my dreams.

I was done doing what people thought I should do.

I was done doing what was expected of me.

I was done pleasing other people.

At first, my husband wasn't thrilled with my new attitude or my quest to do what I wanted. But once he realized I wasn't backing down and was serious about quitting my job and focusing on my family and writing, he came around.

"I had cancer," I would say to him. "I'm not waiting anymore."

He didn't really know how to respond, so he just shrugged and said, "OK."

It's easy to get caught up in the details of life and what you should do. You find yourself spending your life trying to please other people or doing what is expected of you. Responsibilities get in the way. But when you live life trying to please others, you aren't necessarily being true to yourself.

How many times a day do you find yourself using the word "should?" If you're like most people, maybe more often than you would like. There were times in my life when it felt like the word "should," and all it represented, followed me around like my shadow. It came and went throughout my day, seeping into my happiness and stealing pieces of joy when I wasn't looking. The word "should" nagged me. I often felt obligated to make decisions based on what was expected of me instead of what I wanted to do. Fortunately, the word "should" doesn't have a place in my life anymore. When it tries to worm its way in, not only am I good at recognizing it, I'm willing to do something about it.

Obviously, life is filled with responsibilities and there are many things we do in our lives out of necessity—work, driving carpool, going to the doctor, paying our bills. I'm not referring to these types of things. Ditching your responsibilities or slacking off in your life is definitely not what I'm suggesting. I'm talking about the little "shoulds" that seem to get in the way of life sometimes: "I'm tired and I don't want to go to the meeting, but I should." "I don't feel like going to the party, but I should." "I want to take a trip now but I should wait."

It isn't hard to come up with things we should do. I'm guessing if you thought about it, you could probably come up with a few you experienced just this week. Consider this your little reminder to stop trying to please other people. Instead, figure out what you want from your life and find a way to get it.

It's like a switch flipped in me after cancer. I stopped comparing myself to other people. I stopped looking at other people for their approval on the decisions I was making for my life. I gave myself permission to stop trying to live up to other people's standards. When I learned to do this, a huge weight was lifted off my shoulders. It's exhausting to try and please other people all the time. It's also impossible. I realized I could spend a lot of time trying or I could commit to living my best life. This isn't being selfish, by the way, it's living honestly.

It all comes down to priorities. Before breast cancer, I felt like I had to be perfect. I never asked for help. I always felt I had to look a certain way, act a certain way, come across a certain way. It was important to me to impress people. I wanted approval from others. It fed my soul and drove me to accomplish more and more. I looked like I had it all together: perfect kids, house, husband, life. Only I didn't, not even close. When you're standing in an emergency room, bald and holding a bin of vomit, the perfect image goes away.

Our society likes to measure things, and success is one of them. We do this by looking at dollar signs, job titles and house size. It's easy to get caught up in comparing yourself to the achievements of other people, but be careful. You don't want to spend your life working hard to accomplish someone else's dreams. You have to define success for yourself and then have the courage to follow your heart, to create the life you want. People aren't bashful about exploiting their materialism or expensive possessions, or making other people feel inadequate in order to make themselves feel superior. My experience taught me I'm much happier when I don't worry about what other people expect me to do, but instead, live life so it feels right to me. I look at how I'm spending my time and the quality of my relationships. Am I being true to my passions? Am I making the most of my time and spending it on what truly matters to me?

I'm a lot happier today because of this realization. For me, success is about living a balanced and authentic life. A life that feels comfortable. I measure success by the laughter I hear coming from my children's rooms, the satisfaction I feel when we're having fun together and the feeling I get in my heart when I know I'm connecting with the people I love. I hope I'm making the world a little brighter and maybe helping other people along the way. Focusing on my blog, writing my books and connecting with people from around the world feels right, and that's enough. I don't need a big paycheck to make me feel like I'm making a difference. I don't need a title or corner office to feel valued.

Even though life is uncertain, you can still figure out what's important to you and what your priorities are, then make decisions to help keep yourself on your path. But don't wait too long or you might never get the chance to do it. While there will be challenges and road blocks, hard decisions to be made, and even second-guessing about some of your choices, once you figure out what you want from your life, you're more likely to get it.

Life is fragile and unpredictable, but even with its imperfections, it is still the most wonderful prize of all. Every day we get to wake up and move forward, doing the best we can with what we've been given. After cancer, I was ready to live my life on my own terms, and I had finally figured out what that meant.

Life doesn't go exactly as we expect. Trust me, this isn't the first book I thought I would write. I never planned on writing a book about cancer. But I've stopped locking myself into certain expectations and I'm open to all the possibilities life has to offer. Be willing to give up any preconceived notions of what you thought your life would be like. Accept that things don't usually work out the way we planned. Enjoy it when life becomes even better than you imagined.

TIP 43: NO ONE HAS A PERFECT LIFE

Life is never going to be perfect. There will always be ups and downs and everyone has challenges. But you can intentionally decide to help yourself. How do you do this? Instead of dwelling on your problems, count your blessings. If you feel like you're struggling a bit and you aren't content with your current situation, there are things you can do to help yourself.

Here's what you can do to improve your life, starting right now:

- Have a positive attitude.

- Count your blessings.

- Smile instead of frown.

- Be nice instead of grumpy.

- Get enough sleep.

- Spend your time doing something you love.

- Find a way to help someone else.

- Surround yourself with people who bring out the best in you.

- Work hard.

- Focus on what you have, not what you don't.

- Fail and be willing to try again.

- Take care of yourself, exercise and eat well.

- Give yourself alone time to write in a journal or think about your life.

- Try something new.

- Pick yourself up when you fall down.

TIP 44: MAKE YOURSELF A PRIORITY

I can fill the pages of this book telling you to make yourself a priority. I can encourage you to go after your dreams and follow your heart. I can say it over and over again, but ultimately you have to decide to move forward and take action. Don't wait for a special occasion or put off doing what you really want to do. If there's one thing I learned on this journey, it's that life is uncertain and time is precious. Use your time wisely and well, seize the day and be willing to make yourself a priority. I know there are probably other people in your life you're responsible for, but your dreams are important too. Remember, tomorrow isn't guaranteed for anyone. Don't put off doing something you really want to do because you think you'll have more time or money in the future. You might not ever get to do it.

TRIBE TIP

When someone hears the words, "You have cancer," everything changes. Don't be surprised if your friend or family member sees things differently and wants to make some life changes. They might be ready to stop putting off things they've always wanted to do. They might be dabbling in things you never even knew they were interested in. You might be thinking, "What in the world are they doing?" Be patient and try to be flexible. Recognize they might want to go after their dreams, hard. Once someone goes through cancer, he or she understands time is precious.

Your future is
whatever you have
the courage to make it.

CHAPTER 24

BE OPTIMISTIC ABOUT YOUR FUTURE

After cancer, I was scared for my future. I obsessed about it. I worried that because of this part of my past, my future was doomed. I was afraid cancer would take my life and I wouldn't be there to watch my daughters grow up. I had to somehow accept that having cancer at 42 was always going to be part of my story and stop focusing on it.

If you're struggling with your past, I understand. But you need to do yourself a big favor and let it go. You aren't what you've done or what you've been through. We all have things in our past we don't like, something we wish hadn't happened. Here's the bottom line: You can carry your past around and let it get in the way of making the most of the rest of your life, or you can decide to let it go.

I don't like that cancer is part of my story. I want to delete it from my record. But as hard as I try, I'm not going to be able to remove this part, or any part, of my past. So I can either dwell on it, be angry and bitter about it, or accept it happened and be grateful I'm a survivor. I can be laser-focused on the negative parts of my past or remember the big picture and embrace it all—the good and the bad.

If life hasn't been kind to you, if you feel you've been wronged, you must make peace with it. You'll be happier, calmer and more fun to be around. You'll also be more likely to move into your future with the ability to make the most of your life. If you're walking around carrying a heavy bag filled with anger, guilt or despair, it's time to toss it aside and move forward. Don't dwell on what you don't like about being diagnosed with cancer, find something good that came from it and commit to making the most of the rest of your life.

If you're thinking, "There's no way I can make peace with my past and put it behind me," I'm here to tell you that you can. How? You actively decide to accept what happened in your past and focus your time and energy on the present. Accepting what happened doesn't mean you like it. Believe me, I'm not happy I got cancer and had to have surgeries, chemo and radiation. But I eventually accepted it. I also stopped blaming myself for my cancer and forgave my body for getting it. Once I did this, I could truly start to heal.

I didn't realize it when I was going through my treatment, but I was smack dab in the middle of learning some pretty amazing lessons about life, what truly mattered to me and how strong I actually am. I was getting a first-hand look at what it felt like to be humble. My experience was making me a more compassionate and empathetic person. I was learning how to recognize all the blessings in my life instead of taking them for granted. Crushing cancer was hard, but that doesn't mean there weren't good things that came from it.

You must not focus on the negative moments, your failures or the things you regret about your past.

You must not make your life about the bad things that happened to you.

You are not what you've been through.

You are not a victim.

Often, when we experience a negative situation, we don't just live it once. We replay it over and over again in our minds. It's a story we like to tell ourselves. Like watching old reruns or movies on TV, we know what is going to happen. Maybe we think if we keep obsessing about it, the outcome will change. Or perhaps it's a way to punish ourselves. Whatever the reasoning is, I've tried it and I'm here to tell you it doesn't work. I spent a lot of time going over my experience in my mind. I thought about it a lot. Guess what? Nothing changed.

I eventually figured out I wasn't helping myself or anyone around me by continuously reliving my past. Instead, it just kept cancer in the forefront of my mind. I was filling my head with negativity instead of focusing on the blessings in my life. I realized holding onto my past and punishing myself for whatever I regretted wasn't a healthy way to live, that it would eat at me and destroy all the good I have to offer.

What has happened has happened.

Accept it.

Make peace with it.

Decide to learn from your past. Use this knowledge to help yourself live better going forward. One day you might even be able to help someone else because of what you've been through. Sadly, the older I get, the more frequently I hear about people I know who are facing their own diagnosis. When this happens, I try to reach out to them because I've been there. I know how hard it is to go through cancer. I can share what I've learned with them and hopefully help make their experience a little easier.

After my diagnosis and treatments, I decided I wanted to volunteer at the hospital where I had been treated, specifically in the chemotherapy room. It was one of the best decisions I ever made. Going to the chemo room each Friday morning, just for a few hours, has brought me so much joy. When people come in, especially for the first time, they're scared. They don't know what to expect. They don't know how the chemo will affect them. There are a lot of uncertainties when it comes to cancer. When I say to someone, "I was sitting in that same chair once, and now look at me," I see them visibly relax.

Often, the patient will ask, "Really, you had cancer?"

"Yes," I say. "I got through it, and so will you."

I talk to them about whatever they want, answering their questions and offering support. It is my privilege to be able to help them. It has made me a more compassionate and understanding person, and I feel good helping them and thinking about someone else besides myself. It's also a weekly reminder that life is precious and I shouldn't take anything for granted.

Once you know deep in your heart you've dealt with your past, accepted what happened and forgiven yourself, that's when you can really start to live in the present. A year after I went through my experience I went to a spa and met with a counselor there. She told me something I'll never forget. We were talking about how scared I was about my future and how I was exhausted from focusing on cancer.

"Dara," she said, "Once you're able to talk about your experience without feeling anxious or stressed, that's how you know you've really made peace with what you've been through."

I asked, "Do you really think that will ever happen?"

Her answer was simple, "Be patient and give it time."

She was right. The more time went by, the easier it became to talk about my experience and process what I'd been through. To stop being afraid and look to the future with excitement.

Life is uncertain. For me, for you, for all of us. If we thought about all of the bad things that could happen to us each day, we wouldn't leave our homes or let our kids out of our sight. That is no way to live. We can't let fear take over. We have to believe things will turn out well, focus on what we can control and let go of worry.

I don't have a crystal ball and I can't predict the future. I'm guessing you can't either. If you've been through cancer, you might feel a little unsettled about your future. OK, maybe a lot unsettled. You might be afraid you're going to get cancer again. Anxiety might be following you around and holding you back. Here's what I want you to remember: there are no guarantees for anyone. Are you listening? Anything can happen to anyone at any time. As a cancer survivor, you know how precious life is. You understand how each day of your life is a true gift. Make sure you aren't wasting it. Don't walk around worrying about what might possibly happen to you. Worrying isn't going to help anything. Instead, decide to be optimistic about your future. Put your energy into living your best life and making the most out of each day. Allow yourself to live fully. We worry about a lot of things in our lives and most of the time we don't ever experience what we wasted our time worrying about. Instead, enjoy the here and now and be optimistic about all the good things coming down the road. You owe it to yourself to live this way.

TIP 45: USE YOUR EXPERIENCE TO HELP OTHER PEOPLE

Unfortunately, there are many people who are diagnosed with cancer every day. Hearing about other people who have been diagnosed with cancer has become a normal part of life. Too often even my kids will say to me, "My friend so-and-so's mom was diagnosed with cancer," or "So-and-so's father has this kind of cancer. What do you think about it?" We can't stop cancer from happening, but we can help people who are going through it. Reach out to people who are facing cancer and try to help them. Call them, offer to meet them for coffee, go to their homes to sit and talk. Share what you learned on your journey. Give them support and guidance and show them a person can have cancer and get to the other side of it. Don't underestimate how beneficial this can be to someone who has just been diagnosed. They can see how well you're doing and it will empower them. They will think, "She went through what I'm going through and look at how well she's doing now. If she can do it, so can I."

Children who have watched a parent go through cancer can be very helpful to other kids who have a parent who has been diagnosed. If your kids are willing and able, encourage them to help and be supportive. When we stop focusing on ourselves and start helping other people, it makes us feel good. This is beneficial for everyone.

TRIBE TIP

If you know someone who has been diagnosed with cancer, encourage your friend or family member to be open to talking with that person. This can help in three ways:

It will help your friend or family member realize how good it feels to help another person. It's cathartic to open up and talk about your experience. When someone is sharing their story and telling someone else what they learned and went through, they're also getting it out instead of keeping it bottled inside. This is how we make peace with what happened and put it behind us.

It will help get them out of their own head. Focusing your energy on how you can assist someone else is a great way to stop obsessing about yourself.

It is empowering to realize you can inspire and offer hope to another person.

The best things in life
can't be bought.
They have to be felt,
like love and
friendship.

CHAPTER 25

LOVE WITH ALL YOUR HEART

There aren't a lot of free things in life that are in abundant supply or will never run out. Thank goodness love is one of them. The amount of love we have isn't finite. We can open our hearts to everyone around us and still have space in our hearts and lives to let others in.

Love is what makes life meaningful. The relationships we have with the people we care about is truly what matters. Letting people into our lives, opening up and connecting with other people can bring a tremendous amount of joy.

But love doesn't come without risk.

There is always the risk of losing someone we love. When we give a piece of our heart to another person, there's always a chance we will get hurt. The same holds true for the people who love and care about us.

When my mom passed away, I could actually feel my heart aching. For the first time in my life, I truly understood what it meant to have a broken heart. I was sad and angry and never wanted to feel that way again. I wanted to withhold my love from the other people in my life, love more cautiously. It felt safer. So I distanced myself, figuring that way, if I lost someone I loved or something bad happened to them, it wouldn't hurt as much. But in reality, I was hurting myself. I was closing off my relationships and not fully experiencing the joy that comes from loving others. I was also wasting the precious time I had with the people I cared about.

I was trying to protect myself from the pain that comes when we lose someone we love. This wasn't a very mature way to act. Instead of leaning on the people I loved the most and who could help me deal with my grief, I thought I'd just go it alone. It didn't work very well. Actually, it made me feel worse. Now I was sad about my mom's death and lonely. Fortunately, I came around eventually and recognized this wasn't how I wanted to live. I realized it was the people in my life that made it worth living. Trying to protect myself from being hurt again wasn't doing anything but making me feel isolated.

The same was true when I was diagnosed with cancer. I couldn't have gone through it by myself and, fortunately, I didn't try to. I was too upset to put on airs or walk around pretending everything was fine. It wasn't. I let other people see me scared and sad. I was willing to talk about how I felt and what I was afraid of and to be honest with the people I loved. Looking back, some of the best conversations I've ever had with my friends and family took place during this time. We shared our greatest fears and talked about what truly mattered to each of us. We cried together and hugged one another. In the end, it was the love of those around me that helped get me through when I didn't have the courage to move forward.

I'm not going to lie to you, there were definitely times I took my anxiety out on the people I love the most. I would snap or be grumpy, overreact or transfer my negative feelings onto them. How fortunate for them, right? Here's the thing, this type of behavior, while not ideal, is very normal. When something is bothering us, we tend to lash out at our "safe" people. That doesn't mean it's right, it just is what it is. My husband was the lucky recipient of most of my mood swings.

Often, he would say, "When you're ready to talk about this, I'll be happy to talk. Until then, I'll give you a little space."

This was the best way to deal with me because he wasn't reacting to my moods. He wasn't giving me what I wanted, which was an argument. I wanted to feed my anger, but he was smart and didn't allow little disagreements to escalate. It's hard to fight with another person when they leave the room.

Often, we would just laugh about it after I calmed down. I would feel guilty about my behavior and try to apologize, but he wasn't having any of it.

"I know this is a hard time for you," he would say.

I've already told you my husband, Jon, is a saint. Don't think for a second though that there weren't times when I pushed him so hard he yelled back and we argued. I'm not perfect, he's not perfect, no relationship is perfect.

I grew up in a family where we always said, "I love you" to one another. Sometimes, we would be in our bedrooms at night and we would shout it throughout the house. So I've always been open with my feelings. But after cancer I started saying "I love you" to everyone in my life. I never want anyone I care about to question how I feel about them. I don't toss the word around lightly—when I say "I love you," I mean it—but I make sure to let the people I love know it on a regular basis. I say it to the people I care about every time I hang up the phone or part ways.

Just as I wanted to shower the people I care about with love and spend more time with them, I also wanted to actively decide who I wanted to be around. I found I didn't have a lot of patience for some of the people I used to have a lot in common with. We had outgrown each other, not because they did something wrong or suddenly became bad people, but because my priorities had changed.

I wanted to spend my time with people I truly cared about. I no longer had any tolerance for petty gossip or silly confrontations. Acquaintances or casual friendships didn't seem that important anymore. I wanted to spend my time with real friends. It was a little unsettling when I first realized this. I didn't want to toss aside lifelong friendships just because I didn't think we could relate to one another anymore, but at the same time, I wanted to be with people who made me feel good about myself and built me up. I didn't need to be with anyone who was negative or brought me down. I wanted to be around positive people who were optimistic and upbeat and who I could be myself around. I was done trying to impress people. I had become a "what-you-see-is-what-you-get" kind of person, and it was empowering. It felt good to be myself.

I wasn't afraid to pull away from negative people or end relationships that entailed a lot of unnecessary drama. However, I didn't want to make a scene about it. I simply backed off. I didn't call or text them as frequently and we got together less and less. Over time, it all sorted itself out. When I stopped spending time with negative people, something amazing happened. It opened up space in my life for new people to come into my life, people who I had a lot in common with now and who had similar priorities and interests. The saying, "You are who you associate with," is absolutely true. I wanted to be with positive, upbeat, inspiring people.

Life is more fun when you have true friends to share it with. It's the difference between simply living life and squeezing out every last morsel of joy. Even if you're someone who enjoys being alone, you still need people in your life.

People who care about you.

People who will be there for you when life gets rough.

People who don't judge you and who accept the real you.

As a cancer patient, when I saw my life flash before my eyes and felt scared or sick, it wasn't things that helped me feel better. It was the people who cared about me. People who gave me courage and were there for me to lean on. While it's fun to have things, and I certainly enjoy my fair share of retail therapy, I know materialism will never take center stage in my life. In fact, after cancer, I noticed I became very selective about what I owned. I wanted to simplify my life and get rid of all the stuff that was bringing me down or that I didn't really like. I cleaned out the clutter and made a point to surround myself with things that made me happy. It feels good to simplify and only have what I truly like in my life.

I also wanted my home to be a happy and cozy environment that made me feel safe. A place in the world that grounded me and where my family and I could be comfortable. A place where I could work to become the best version of myself. When I was almost done with my treatment, I set aside an area in my home where I could meditate, practice yoga, write in my journal and connect with my thoughts. It's open and light and makes me feel happy whenever I go there. I've worked out a lot of things in that room, and I'm thankful to have it.

TIP 46: HEAL YOUR HEART

If you've loved and lost, hold on tightly to the memories you have. Move on with your life, taking those you've lost with you. I know it isn't easy. Losing someone dear to you can make you want to lock the door to your heart and toss away the key. You've got to work through it and learn to trust again, to love again. It took me a little time to come to terms with this, but I now know I'll always choose to love, even though it comes with the risk of losing the people I care for. I'd rather make the most of my time by letting people into my life than shutting them out to protect myself.

TIP 47: SAY "I LOVE YOU" TO THE PEOPLE YOU LOVE

Don't hold back when it comes to telling other people how you feel. When you love someone, let them know. Tell them how much they mean to you and how blessed you feel to have them in your life. I've met many people who have never heard their parents or partner say the words, "I love you." Because of this, they tend to do the same with the people in their lives. If this sounds familiar, change it right now. Stop the pattern. Decide today to make sure the people you love and care about know exactly how you feel every day of your life. Don't hold back. You'll be surprised how good it feels to open up and let people know you care about them. I'd be willing to bet once you start opening up and telling people how you feel about them, they'll return the favor. It feels good to say "I love you," and even better to hear it.

TIP 48: WATCH WHO YOU HANG WITH

You deserve to have friends who love and support you through good times and bad. Find those people who accept you for who you are, who see you at your worst and love you anyway, who bring out the best in you and who are there for you even when it isn't convenient. It can take time and energy to figure out where you fit in. Put yourself in situations where you are likely to meet people you have something in common with, people who see the world like you do and who share similar values and priorities.

Don't assume you'll never find your tribe. There are plenty of support groups for people who are going through cancer or have survived cancer. Be willing to attend these meetings and open up to others you meet on your journey. There are lessons to be learned from everyone you come into contact with. Pay attention to the people who cross your path. Life is full of amazing and wonderful people. Be open to meeting these people and filling your life with those who love and cherish you.

We all know negative people. People who are critical and judgmental and have a glass-half-empty view of life. They expect the worst and want everyone around them to know it. While we can't control the behavior of other people, we can absolutely control how we react to the negativity. We can also try to limit the amount of time we spend with those who bring us down.

If someone is in a grumpy mood and is saying mean things, simply walk away if you can. Go into another room, go for a walk, put on your earphones and tune them out. Do whatever it takes to prevent the negativity from seeping into your space. Sometimes laughing about a particular situation is the best way to diffuse it. If you're with someone who's having a temper tantrum, not taking it too seriously can be a way to get them to lighten up. You'll have to feel your way through this one, but I've noticed it can help the person realize they need to ditch the negativity. And even if they don't see it, at least you'll be getting a good laugh.

Try talking to the person who is being negative about how their mood is affecting the people around them. Hopefully the person will be willing to hear what you have to say and be receptive to the feedback. If they get defensive or deny what you're saying, your only choice is to let it go and move on. You can only do so much to help another person see how their actions are impacting those around them. If they don't want to acknowledge it, you're wasting your energy trying to convince them. The best thing you can do is focus on what you can control—yourself.

If there are people in your life who are saying negative things to you about your prognosis, you need to nicely shut it down. You need positive people cheering you on, not negative people who make you feel badly about things. I can't stress this enough. You have enough to deal with right now, you don't need to add negative people to the list.

TRIBE TIP

The best thing you can do to help someone you care about thrive after cancer is to shower them with love. Recognize they're fragile and vulnerable. They're scared and need an extra dose of kindness. Do everything you can to build them up. Be positive and loving. Watch what you say to them and how you say it. Tell them how much you care about them and how you're there for them. Listen when they want to talk. If they're short with you or sensitive, remember it isn't about you, it's about what they're going through. Be willing to look the other way if they snap at you or get grumpy. Remember, we tend to take out our anxiety and stress on the people we love the most. You don't deserve to be treated like a doormat, but try to let some things slide.

Be kind. Be nice.
Smile often, even at people
you don't know.
Laugh loudly. At yourself.
Enjoy each day, every moment.
Take nothing for granted.

CHAPTER 26

FIND MEANING EACH DAY

Life is made up of different seasons. I never understood this until I went through my cancer journey. If we're lucky, when we get to the end of our lives, the happy seasons will outnumber the sad ones and the beautiful memories we have with our loved ones will be what stand out in our minds. There are lessons to be learned, regardless of where we are in our lives or what season we find ourselves in. We just have to be willing to see them, to open our eyes to the messages the universe sends our way.

We don't have a lot of control over which season we find ourselves facing. Getting through the hard times—the difficult seasons that feel nearly impossible and cause us to question everything—helps us grow and become stronger. It's also when we learn to fully appreciate the joyful moments. From suffering comes a deep appreciation for all the blessings in life, and this is what makes life truly meaningful.

Too many people define themselves by one experience. They become what happened to them instead of the person they are. Because of this, they hold themselves back and never get to be the person they were meant to be. We're each a culmination of our environment and all of our experiences, not just one. The person you are today is a direct result of where you've been and what you've been through. This doesn't mean you're defined by your past, it just means it had an impact on you. How could it not? There's no denying that some experiences leave a longer-lasting mark. Usually it's the big events we tend to remember more than others, good or bad. The special moments in life such as weddings, the birth of a child, the day you met your partner, or graduated from high school or college. Times like these typically take center stage in our memory bank. Then there are the other moments, the ones we wish had never happened. The loss of a loved one, the end of a relationship, a cancer diagnosis. We can't choose what we remember, but we can decide how to process what we've been through and how it will affect our future.

My cancer journey is one of those experiences that will always stand out in my mind. I will always remember that season of my life: the people I met, the challenges I faced, how scared I was. But, I'll also remember how strong it made me and how much better I live today because of what I went through. When I look back on my life, the times that were the most difficult presented the greatest chance for me to grow and become a better version of myself. I learned the most when I pushed myself forward, didn't give up and learned to trust everything would be OK.

The more time goes by, the more distance I put between me and the ugly couch I sat on the day I heard the words, "You have cancer," the easier it is to block out what my family and I went through. But I know I'll never completely forget that time in my life because

I don't want to. The lessons I learned are too valuable to ever forget. In fact, every day of the rest of my life will be better because of my experience with cancer. And for that I'll always be grateful.

When you go through hard times, you have two choices. You can push forward and overcome them, or you can let them take you down and get in the way of your enjoyment of life. Most of us don't stop to think about all we have unless something happens that forces us to do so. Surviving cancer will force you to look at everything differently. You will be a changed person. You'll be able to see what your priorities are and what you want to do with the rest of your life. Allow yourself to process what you've been through and learn from it.

Life can be hard. It can make you angry and bitter. You can get so pissed off about whatever it is you have to deal with you become a person no one wants to be around, someone you don't even recognize. You might even want to quit. You might say to yourself, "This is just too damn hard. I don't want to do this. I can't do this." It's OK if you've had these thoughts. Believe me, I think anyone dealing with cancer questions themselves, especially in those low moments when we think there's no way we can survive.

I'm a cancer survivor. This isn't a label I ever wanted, and if you have been diagnosed with cancer, I know it's a label you probably aren't excited to have either. But it sure is better than the alternative. If you are still working through your treatment, here's what you need to do:

Hang on to faith and trust everything will work out.

Fight like hell and don't give up.

Take one day at a time and tell yourself you can get through whatever it is you're facing.

Expect good things to happen.

Expect to win.

Expect to crush cancer.

Your attitude will play a huge role in how you do. Decide to be positive. Believe you're going to beat the statistics, especially if they aren't in your favor. Know you can get through it and allow yourself the opportunity to learn all the lessons that are there for the taking.

And after you survive, let yourself thrive. Don't be afraid to live honestly and authentically, being the best version of yourself. Show up to the world with kindness and love. Actively decide how you want to spend your time and who you want to be with. Surround yourself with people you love and follow your passions. Don't just go through the motions, really show up. Be present when you're with your kids, family and friends. Make memories. Laugh with each other. Really talk. Engage. Be able to see the joy in everyday life and don't take anything for granted. It's in the ordinary moments, the normal day-to-day parts of life, that you can have an extraordinary connection with the people you love, but only if you make it happen.

Focus your energy on the present moment, and look to the future with positivity and possibility. I can't begin to tell you how much I've changed since that day on the ugly couch. A lot has happened in my life since I heard the words, "You have cancer." Truth be told, I'm a lot happier today than I was before cancer. The joy

I experience each day of my life is something I savor and appreciate. My laugh is louder, I smile a lot more and I'm living a more authentic life.

People often ask me if I'm glad I got cancer. I'm not glad, but I absolutely live better today because of it. If there was a way for me to not get cancer and still be the person I am today, I would definitely sign up for that. But it doesn't work that way. You have to take the bad with the good. I've accepted this is my journey, and I'm dedicated to making it all count, every single part of it.

I hope my story will stay with you, that you'll remember my words when you find yourself getting frustrated, stressed out or overwhelmed. When fear stares you in the face and you don't know what to do. I know that fear. I've felt it, lived it. Remember, in the hard seasons of life, if you can hold on to faith and trust things will be OK, you're more likely to get to the other side.

No one knows what the future holds. You can let fear get in the way of enjoying your life or you can take this knowledge and commit to living each day to the fullest. You can decide to take the time each day to connect with the people you love, strengthen your relationships and live without regret. Life isn't perfect, but it's worth fighting for, even when it gets hard.

TIP 49: DECIDE TO MAKE THE REST OF YOUR LIFE COUNT

Whatever you've been through and whatever your past looks like, decide today to make the most of the rest of your life. Wasting time feeling sorry for yourself isn't going to help you. You can have a pity party and bask in your sorrow, or you can decide to do something about it. That's what separates the ones who thrive from the ones who let life get the best of them. Don't be one of those people who goes down without a fight. Instead, decide to overcome whatever challenge you're facing and fight hard. You aren't a quitter. When life feels too overwhelming, break it down and focus on today. Do whatever you can to help yourself overcome the current obstacle in your path. Sometimes we get too caught up in the future and we forget to just take one day at a time. If you get dealt a hand you never asked for and one you don't think you can overcome, change your thinking. Focus on your strengths instead of your weaknesses. Find something to be grateful for, even if it takes you an hour to come up with it. You're stronger than you think.

TIP 50: FIND MEANING EACH DAY

Every day we have the chance to look for moments with meaning. Make sure you travel through life with your eyes open so you will recognize the extraordinary in the ordinary. It's in the normalcy of life that the truly important moments tend to show up. Don't miss them! Appreciate all the beauty that surrounds you. Connect with the people you love. Commit to finding meaning every day for the rest of your life. I don't know how long you or I will live or what our futures hold. What I do know is we can actively decide to make each day count.

I will, will you?

SPECIAL THANKS

Thank you for taking the time to read *Crush Cancer*. I've been as open and honest as possible in sharing my story and I hope my words have helped you, wherever you are on your journey. Although a cancer diagnosis isn't something you wanted, it's something you can get through and learn from. It's not easy, but then again, most things in life aren't. Always remember, you are stronger than you think and you can deal with whatever challenges life tosses your way. Believe you can and will crush cancer!

Much love,

Dara

ACKNOWLEDGEMENTS

To Jon, my loving husband of almost 25 years. When we met in college, those two kids could never have known all the wonderful and hard times we would face together. I am thankful for your constant love and support, for being by my side in good and bad, and for always having faith in me. Sharing my life with you is a true blessing and we will never have enough time together.

To my wonderful and loving parents who always told me I could do anything I wanted to do and who believed in me. You always led by example and served as inspiring people to look up to. It's a privilege to be your daughter. I miss Mom every day, but carry her with me and know she is smiling down at me. I don't know what I would do without you, Dad. Your level-headed guidance and never-ending unconditional love grounds me. You have taught me how to make the most of each day of my life. I cherish our time together, our talks and walks, and deep friendship.

Thanks to my stepmother, Lois, for loving me like her daughter and being my friend. And for rubbing my shoulders when I was throwing up. That's true love.

To my in-laws, Suzy and Arthur, who have known me since I was 18 and have always been there for me, cheering me on and supporting me. Thank you for showering me with unconditional love. You are a blessing in my life and I love you.

To my brother Ari, thank you for being my brother and friend. I cherish our conversations as we strive to help other people and grow ourselves.

To Meggie, my sister-in-law, David, my brother-in-law, and Sarah and James, my step-siblings, I love traveling through life with you, our long talks, and being friends as well as siblings. You inspire me.

To my Richmond family, Shelli, Bob, Bonnie, Uncle Jack, Bette and Gary, and all my extended cousins and family. Thank you for your love and support.

To my Winston-Salem family, thank you for helping me during one of the hardest times of my life and for your constant willingness to lend a hand and be there for me.

To Garth, the napkin notes dad. Thank you for meeting me for coffee that first time, and for all of the deep conversations we've had since then. I never could have imagined what a special friend you would become. I admire you, your perseverance and your selfless love for your family. Thank you for being my dear friend.

To Steven Aitchison and my YDF family. Thank you for being in my life, navigating this road with me and for showing your love and support. Because of you, I had the courage to finish this book, move forward with it, and do everything else. You are my tribe and I am forever grateful for each of you.

To the YDF Accountability buddies. I've shared more with you than I have with some of my oldest friends. Thank you for your love and support and your much-needed suggestions and guidance.

To my mommy tribe, my partners in crime, the strong women I'm blessed to call my friends. You know who you are. I don't know what I would do without you. You are my people. You've seen me at my lowest and loved me through it. You make life more fun and bring me such joy and happiness. Plus, you know all my secrets. To my Maj group, oh how I love our weekly lunch and play, and especially our conversations.

To the teams at UniMedia and Publish Pros. You had faith in me and were willing to take a risk on a girl with a dream. To Rich and Richie, thank you for your amazing ideas, out-of-the-box thinking and for going down this road with me. I am one lucky girl.

To my editor, Mary. Thank you for your brilliant guidance, your patience and your ability to help me communicate my words in the best possible manner. The final product wouldn't be as amazing if you hadn't added your magic.

To my doctors, nurses, counselors and health care providers. Thank you for your patience and support during one of the most challenging times in my life. Your knowledge, expertise and guidance has been and always will be deeply appreciated.

Thank you to all the brave souls who were willing to participate in clinical trials so we have the treatments that are available today. I wouldn't be alive if it weren't for you.

To the cancer patients I met on my journey who are no longer with us. You came into my life for a reason and left your mark on me. I will never forget you.

To my followers on my blog, Crazy Perfect Life, and on social media. You bring me so much joy and happiness and our interaction is a blessing in my life. Thank you for following me and being part of my Crazy Perfect Life.

AUTHOR BIO

After being diagnosed with breast cancer at age 42, Dara left her 20-year career as a personal banker and financial planner to focus on writing, speaking and mentoring.

Her popular blog, "Crazy Perfect Life," reaches over 175,000 followers across the globe through her website and social media. She is a frequent contributor to *The Huffington Post* and is a columnist for *Forsyth Woman Magazine*.

In addition to writing, Dara shares her inspirational words by speaking at events for medical centers and civic groups. She also provides individualized mentoring for those learning to cope with their own cancer diagnoses.

Dara currently lives in Lewisville, North Carolina with her husband, Jon, and their two teenage daughters, Zoe and Avi.

Visit Dara online at www.crazyperfectlife.com and on social media.

ONE-ON-ONE CANCER COACHING

It's individualized! It doesn't matter where you are on your journey. Dara can help you fiure out what you need and devise a plan that caters solely to you.

It's empowering! You are not what you've been through. You are not cancer. You are not a victim. Dara will help you process what is happening and make peace with your diagnosis.

It's therapeutic! Let Dara will share with you what worked for her and help you establish a personalized daily stress and care routine so you can ditch the fear and bring focus to your life.

It's effective! There are lessons to learn from any experience, and going through cancer treatment isn't any different. Dara will help you recognize the valuable takeaways from your experience.

It's not complicated! Dara will break things down, make it simple, and give you weekly assignments and tools to help you move forward faster than you would if you were going at it alone.

Visit CrazyPerfectLife.com/mentor
to SIGN UP or learn more!

CPSIA information can be obtained
at www.ICGtesting.com
Printed in the USA
LVOW13s1952011117
554607LV00014B/2039/P